Trevor Hoyle

Q: Seeking the
Mythical Future

The first novel in the 'Q' series

Panther

Granada Publishing Limited
First published in Great Britain in 1977
by Panther Books Ltd
Frogmore, St Albans, Herts AL2 2NF

A Panther Original
Copyright © Northern Writers 1977
Made and printed in Great Britain by
Cox & Wyman Ltd, London, Reading and Fakenham
Set in Intertype Plantin

For Nick Austen, for believing.

'The cup might smash and *then* fall.'

Aphorism from *A Lay Guide to Myth Technology* (VII Sdp Edition, 3rd Revision)

Contents

I

The Red Ocean

The vessel cleaved through the red ocean, the purple foam churning and frothing in its wake. It was a three-masted barque, square-rigged on the fore- and main-mast, schooner-rigged on the mizzen, with yellow vinyl sails, its prow a whorled piece of timber painted white in the shape of a unicorn's horn: the *Slave Trader*, seventeen days out of London Toun bound for New Amerika in this, the ninth year of the reign of Our Most Gracious King Jimmy K.

For three days the Easterlies had tautened the sails and swept the vessel along at a fine pace, but now, approaching the doldrums, the wind was slackening and within hours would have died to a whisper, barely moving the heavy ship at a rate of two or three knots. A thin haze obscured the yellow orb of the sun, encapsulating the heat so that the breeze along the decks was as warm and fetid as human breath.

Captain Kristiensen stood impassively on the bridge, a tall barrel-chested man with a full black beard who had sailed the oceans since boyhood and knew the tempers and tantrums of the sea, its sly temperament and cunning, and knew also the deeply superstitious nature of the men who sailed it. They were not educated, could neither read nor write, and sought omens and presentiments in the natural phenomena of clouds and waves, birds and sea creatures. Only the day before, a black albatross had circled the main-mast – as the embodiment of an evil spirit might hover round a crucifix – and the crew had watched fearfully in case the bird should decide to land. They could have fired the cannon to scare it away, but that would have prevented the 'spirit' from making a free choice; in effect it would have been cheating on destiny. Instead they had

9

watched silently, and waited with upturned eyes, as the long sweeping arcs of the bird's flight brought it first nearer to the ship and then away from it, approaching and departing, testing their nerves with the perfect symmetry of its swooping glides. Then at last it had flown off: an ominous black hieroglyph heading directly towards a point on the horizon which would eventually be dissected by the descending parabola of the huge yellow sun.

One member of the crew, a Summarian – small, slant-eyed, olive-skinned – said that the black albatross had returned to its master to report their position, course and speed; it was a warning, he said, which they ignored at their peril.

Kristiensen knew of the rumours circulating on board ship but chose to do nothing about them. They were an outlet for the latent fears of the crew, the outward show of collective paranoia which was harmless, providing it didn't erupt into open mutiny. As he said to the First Mate, Mr Standish: 'It almost seems as if the voyage is timed to a nicety, as if the length of it was predetermined in some way. On every trip the sickness reaches the point where it can no longer be contained, when the crew are lethargic and unwilling to work, yet in a very dangerous mood; and then, as always, we sight land.'

The First Mate stepped back from the binnacle, having checked the compass in its brass mounting. He was a young man, this was only his second voyage, and he had great respect and admiration for the Captain. 'There have been mutinies in the past,' he pointed out. 'I read of them in the Nautical Record.'

'That is so,' the Captain agreed, 'but they were usually the fault of the captain, not the crew. An inexperienced man can easily be misled into believing that harsh, repressive measures need to be taken – when in fact quite the reverse applies. These are simple men. They understand clear and direct decisions, but at the same time they are likely to interpret them wrongly, to suppose that a captain dealing harshly with them is doing so through fear and because he has something to hide; therefore a lack of action, indifference almost, can be the correct and sensible approach.'

The young Mr Standish nodded slowly. He could see the wisdom of this, though he also wondered why the Captain thought it necessary – not believing in omens, spirits and demons – to pray each night in his cabin. To whom or what was he praying? And from what horrors of the unknown was he seeking deliverance? Could it be that the black albatross really was a sign of imminent disaster, one they would do well to heed? He felt a vague unease, and despite the enveloping prickly heat the back of his neck was cold and clammy.

On the third day of entering the doldrums they sighted the sea monster. It rose from the red ocean at a distance of approximately three hundred metres: a green scaly neck and massive head with large yellow eyes fixed in a glassy reptilian stare. The crew cowered behind the gunwales, shocked into fearful silence, fingering their holy beads and miming with numbed lips. There was little the Captain could do, for the vessel was practically becalmed on the ponderous swell, the sails hanging wrinkled and flaccid from the sweating booms. Over the entire ocean, from horizon to horizon, there was hardly sufficient movement of air to cause a ripple. He could have ordered the crew to fire on the creature, but the distance was too great, and, instead of frightening it away, might have had the effect of provoking it to attack. If it came any nearer they would have no alternative but to release a broadside yet, knowing the poor accuracy of the fire-weapons (antiquated pieces with primitive sighting devices) and the appalling marksmanship of the gunners, Captain Kristiensen knew very well that the chances of a direct hit were abysmally low.

The First Mate had trained the deck-mounted telescope on the monster and was watching it with a dreadful thrilling fear. It was his first; he had seen sketches and lithographs, heard innumerable eye-witness accounts, but this was his first personal sighting and he was caught between the conflicting emotions of nervous exhilaration and cold abject terror. His throat worked in order to produce saliva for his dry lips.

The creature rode easily on the swell, its yellow saucer-eyes observing the barque with a flat unmoving stare, but making no attempt to approach it. The snake-like neck extended several metres into the air, enlarging to the head and grooved snout below which three concentric rows of backward-facing teeth glinted in the hazy sunlight. The bony diamond-shaped protuberances on its back – hence the name 'Diamond Back' used by the sailors – were plainly visible, appearing as a long line of blunt spikes resting on the surface of the water.

'What do you estimate its length to be?' Mr Standish asked; his excitement and fear were evident in his voice but even so he couldn't bring himself to look away from the eyepiece of the telescope.

'It's a fully-grown plesiosaur,' the Captain answered. 'They can be anything up to eighteen metres and have been known to reach twenty in the southern hemisphere. It's the first you've seen?'

'Yes,' Mr Standish said, mesmerized. He hardly dared breathe. 'Will it attack?'

'If it does we shall part company, you and I.' The Captain tightened his hands into fists and added: 'For a little while.'

The young man was sufficiently intrigued to glance up. He frowned and said, 'For a little while? How is that?'

'We shall part company when the monster attacks and meet up again – very soon, I assure you – in its stomach sac. You see the mouth—' He raised his solid arm and pointed a finger which betrayed no emotion. 'The mouth is hinged so that the lower jaw drops down and acts as a scoop over the surface of the water. It can take three men at a time and can mover faster than a sloop under full sail. There have never been any survivors of an attack by a sea monster. Ships have vanished, wreckage has been found, but never any seamen, living or dead. Not even their remains.'

'So if it attacks our chances are—'

'We have no chances,' Kristiensen replied bluntly. 'What I have told you is not opinion or hearsay, but fact.'

'We can telegraph for help,' Mr Standish said quickly. There was a mist of cold perspiration on his forehead. He was becoming feverish.

'We can do that easily enough,' the Captain conceded. 'We

12

can send a message to any vessel within a radius of sixty leagues. How long do you suppose it would take a ship – if there is one to receive our message – to reach us? And when it arrives, *if* it arrives, what could it do? Do you think that if we received a call for help from a vessel being attacked by a sea monster we would rush to its aid? The sensible thing would be to set course in the opposite direction.'

'But our cannon,' Mr Standish said. 'Surely we have the fire-power to kill it, or at least deter it?' There were flecks of foam on his lips now. His eyes were wide but the pupils had contracted to black dots.

'If the creature comes obligingly near and stays in one place long enough then we might just possibly, given God's own luck, score a hit. But Diamond-Backed plesiosaurs are as agile as eels: it could dive, swim under the ship, come up the other side and attack to port while we're still attempting to sight our cannon to starboard.' The Captain smiled grimly. 'Still not convinced?'

The young man turned nervously to gaze out to sea and as he did so the monster dipped its head, the long sinewy neck curving downwards with supple dexterity; the lower jaw came un-hinged and the horizontal, almost rectangular mouth slot began scooping the sea in long gliding strokes. It was fascinating in its patient deliberation.

'My God, it's horrible!' Mr Standish said. He was ashen. 'Does it know we're at its mercy? Does it have a brain capable of any real intelligence?'

Captain Kristiensen crossed his arms, gripping his biceps with strong fingers. He gave the appearance of placidity, almost of unconcern, but a diligent observer would have noticed the faint white marks around his mouth and nostrils: lines of inner strain and fierce self-control. He said: 'Nothing is known of the creature's physiology, we've never even dis-covered a skeleton washed ashore. The seamen believe that the creature has two brains, one in its skull and the other in the base of its tail. But it's unlikely that we shall ever get close enough to learn the truth – close enough for that alone, anyway.'

The Second Mate came up the steps to the bridge and saluted. 'I've primed the cannon, sir, and picked five men who can be trusted not to lose their heads if the monster attacks. The rest are a pack of gibbering idiots. They're cowardly scum and I've told 'em that to their faces.' He jerked a calloused thumb over his shoulder to indicate the men crouching below on the main deck. Mr Swann had risen over fifteen years from ordinary seaman to Second Mate. He had seen monsters before and lived to tell the tale, and though he knew the ship to be virtually helpless should the creature decide to attack he had absolute faith in Captain Kristiensen's qualities of leadership – besides which he believed in his own sense of destiny; he wasn't ready to die yet: the surge of life in his veins was too quick and strong. He glanced from the Captain to the First Mate, and it confirmed what his nostrils could detect: the rancid smell of fear.

'Very good, Mr Swann. We can do no more. Have you checked the line for drift?'

'Not a movement, sir, the cork's dead. We could be on a millpond. The barometer is steady, no change.' He stepped to the rail and spat into the sea; the spittle plopped into the murky red water and remained motionless. The vessel was fixed to the ocean as a fly stuck in treacle.

'What do you reckon, Mr Swann, to sending a telegraph message?' asked the Captain.

The Second Mate forced a cynical grin. 'And scare off any ship within fifty leagues? Aye, damn true, I know where I'd be if a message came through that somebody had sighted a Diamond Back. I'd be gone.' And he pointed away towards the empty horizon, an almost imperceptible demarcation between sea and sky which was lost in the sluggish haze.

Mr Standish said, 'Is it eating or drinking, or what? Why doesn't it do something? It's almost as if there's something ... mekanikal about its movements – so slow and deliberate.' He looked at the others, taking a handkerchief from his sleeve and wiping his face and neck. He couldn't believe that this was actually happening; it had about it the eerie strangeness of a nightmare. Was he really on this deck, here and now, and not dreaming in his deep and comfortable bed in London Toun, wrapped in the arms of a girl? He would wake up in a minute. He pinched himself to wake himself up but nothing happened, nothing had changed, he was still here. The plesiosaur basked seemingly unperturbed some distance from the ship. The sky, the sun, the mist still had their yellow tinge, the ocean its reddish hue. Captain Kristiensen stood with his feet firmly braced on the deck, the Second Mate leaning on the rail, the crew on their knees murmuring prayers and imprecations. Mysterious forces were at work, hidden powers of the unknown, and the First Mate felt intimidated by his ignorance of the natural elements.

Mr Swann turned from the rail and said tersely, 'It's moving.'

It was true. The plesiosaur had slid down into the water so that only its long snaking neck was visible, and had begun to move astern of them, a gentle vee of ripples marking its progress. The neck glided through the water with perfect smoothness, the creature moving away on a dead straight course, without deviation, and within minutes was a speck in the haze almost too faint to be seen.

'Have we seen the last of it?' Mr Standish asked in a voice he didn't recognize as his own. He felt slightly braver. He had seen his first sea monster and was alive to tell of it. What a story it would make!

Kristiensen unfolded his bulky arms, and the places where his hands had been were damp. 'Unless one or both of its brains decides otherwise,' he said shortly. 'Mr Swann.'

'Captain?'

'Break open a cask of black biddy for the crew. They'll need something to wash the fear out of their throats.' He said to the First Mate: 'I expect you could take a strong drink yourself, Mr Standish. We'll retire to my quarters. Mr Swann, when you've issued the ration, post a double-look-out and join us there. It isn't every day a Diamond Back comes a-calling and is polite enough not to eat its hosts.'

Later in the day the faint stirrings of a breeze began to palpate the sagging vinyl canvas. The timbers began once again to creak their welcome song as the barque eased itself slowly into motion: it was barely a movement at first, a few paltry knots, but to everyone on board it seemed as though they were racing into the sun itself.

The cry from the crow's nest and the outstretched arm of the look-out brought everyone up on deck. The crew took up vantage points in the rigging and scanned the flat sea, shading their eyes from the fierce yellow orb of the sun. 'What is it, Mr Standish?' asked the Captain, emerging from the companion-way on to the quarter-deck, still struggling into his black pigskin jerkin with the golden eagle embossed above the left breast: his captain's insignia.

'Can't make it out, sir.' The First Mate adjusted the brass ferrule on the telescope. 'Appears to be a craft of some sort, quite small, I should judge. It's signalling to us, I think.'

'Let me see.' Kristiensen came forward and squinted into the eyepieces. He was silent for a moment, his lips compressed tightly together. Then he said in a breath, 'Oracles and omens.' It was an exclamation used by the crew, one signifying fear and perplexity, but not what the First Mate would have expected to hear on the Captain's lips.

The barque drew nearer. Through the heat mist it became evident to Mr Standish that what he had taken to be a signal could now be seen as the sun's rays glinting on the hard and polished surface of a small, low craft of shallow displacement floating not so much in the water as on top of it. And as they approached they could see the figure of a man sprawled against the smooth concave incline, his head resting on the rounded lip, one hand trailing in the water. His clothing was stained and tattered, apparently bleached white by the sun.

Kristiensen issued instructions and a boat was lowered. At this distance – less than ten metres – they could see that the craft was made of a material resembling gun-metal. It had the appearance of having been scorched by fire: parts of it were pitted and blistered, with darker areas obscuring the hard bright finish.

'What on this earth do you make of it, sir?' Mr Standish asked the Captain. 'Has he been cast adrift do you suppose?'

He was nearly his old self once more, curious but not frightened; castaways were not as fearsome, and much more easily accommodated, than sea monsters.

'If we, as educated men, believed in omens,' Kristiensen replied with faint irony, 'we might be forgiven for taking this to be the fulfilment of a prophecy. But no doubt we're too rational for that.' He was smiling in a detached fashion.

'What omens do you mean?' the First Mate said.

'Have you forgotten the black albatross we sighted three days ago?'

'No, I hadn't forgotten, but I thought—'

'You thought that to regard it as an omen was straining credulity – that it was a foolish superstition confined to the ignorant and the simple-minded.' He nodded slowly and said softly, as if to himself, 'Perhaps you're right. After many years at sea the sickness seems to spread everywhere like a cancer; sooner or later it affects everyone.'

The First Mate regarded him curiously. He was about to ask which sickness the Captain was referring to when his attention was distracted by the voice of Mr Swann calling from the boat. 'He's alive, Captain. But only just. Heartbeat faint and unsteady.'

'Bring him on board,' Kristiensen ordered. 'Is there anything worth salvaging, supplies, telegraph equipment?'

'It's a shell, that's all,' the Second Mate answered. 'No lockers, sails, no rudder even.' He gestured to one of the seamen, and together they raised and supported the unconscious man and with some difficulty brought him into the longboat. Where he had lain on the shallow concave interior the craft was streaked dark-grey as if seared by flames; and as Kristiensen looked he suddenly stiffened and a tremor passed through him. Partly obliterated by the discoloration, yet still legible, a row of letters in a strange configuration was visible. Kristiensen read them silently, his lips forming the sounds:

R A L

X →

A foreign language perhaps? Certainly the craft was of a type and construction unfamiliar to him. Yet it was just as likely, Kristiensen reasoned, that the letters formed part of words which had been burnt off or otherwise obliterated. He repeated the sequence to commit it to memory, then watched as the longboat returned to the ship and the man was taken on board. Beckoning to the First Mate he went down to the main deck and approached the circle of men that had formed round the supine figure. They fell back and stood silently, curious and yet ill at ease, their eyes shifting restlessly from the Captain to the man lying on the bleached timbers.

He was a tall man, Kristiensen judged, with a strong neck and a robust physique: his features were sharply defined, the nose angular and jutting out from beneath a wide forehead, his hair discoloured from the effects of sun and seawater. There was something odd, too, about his appearance that Kristiensen couldn't quite place until Mr Standish remarked on it – to do with the man's face. It was deathly pale, when by rights it should have been sunburnt. The flesh seemed almost transparent, as if all colour and substance had been washed out of it.

His clothing was also strange. He was dressed in a single piece of material, without seams or fastenings, which fitted him snugly like a second skin from neck to ankles; here and there it was torn and ragged, stained by seawater, and through the rents in the material his skin appeared to glow with an intense paleness and transparency.

Kristiensen knelt down and placed his ear against the man's chest. Barely perceptible, but, yes, there it was: the slow irregular beat of the heart.

He said to Mr Swann: 'Have a bunk made ready. We can save him if we hurry.' He stood up and jerked his head impatiently at the crew: 'Lend a hand here,' but the men clustered in a self-protective group looking fearfully at the pale, scarcely-breathing figure. The voyage had held more than its share of terrors: they were unprepared for sea monsters and even less for the sudden arrival of a man adrift in a strange craft in the dead lost centre of the ocean. It would have been wiser, their attitude implied, to have left him to die: it was tempting the fates to bring on board a man of such unnatural appearance.

Kristiensen tried hard to control his temper. He took a step forward, this time gesturing more emphatically, and the men retreated before him, intimidated by his anger but unwilling to obey.

'I'll shift 'em,' Mr Swann growled. His hand went to his belt where the ivory handle of a knife protruded, but the Captain stopped him with a cautioning hand.

He said softly: 'We needn't resort to force.' Then, addressing the crew in a level and reasonable tone of voice, 'There is no cause to be afraid of this man. I know where he comes from.' There was a stirring of disbelief. 'You've all heard of the airships which New Amerika has constructed to carry passengers and cargo across the sea. This man is a crew member of such an airship, I know this by his uniform. His airship must have been on a voyage over uncharted seas and been blown off course – perhaps it foundered and fell into the sea and this man is the only survivor. There is no reason to be afraid. Surely you don't fear an unconscious man in *this* state of exhaustion? Look at him, is it conceivable that he could do you any harm?'

The men glanced uncertainly at each other. They rubbed their bare feet on the deck in the manner of schoolboys caught in some childish prank. He would shame them into obeying him. Then the Summarian, his dark eyes slitted and evasive, his small tarbrush of a beard close to his chest, shuffled forward a pace or two.

'We didn't bargain for this. There is something bad about this man. I feel it here' – touching his heart with a horny thumb-nail. 'Already we have seen the evil omen, then there was the sea serpent, and now this man floating on the ocean.' His eyes flickered across the Captain's face. 'If he's from an airship of New Amerika, as you say, where are the others who were with him? Why should one man survive and all the others perish?'

Kristiensen held up the broad palms of his hands. 'Who can say? How do we know there aren't other survivors out there somewhere? Take my word, I have no reason to lie to you.' Without waiting for a reaction or giving the Summarian a chance to respond, he turned, saying over his shoulder, 'Take him below, Mr Swann. He must be given immediate attention.'

'One moment, Captain.' The Summarian was not giving in so easily. 'Why is he so pale? He has been exposed to the sun and yet his skin is like a child's.'

'The men who fly the airships are all pale-skinned,' Kristiensen answered. 'It is because they are so high above the clouds. His colour will return in a day or so.' He continued, almost as if it was an afterthought, 'There's likely to be a reward for his safe return; he'll be able to give an eye-witness account of what happened to the airship. Any sum awarded the *Slave Trader* will be divided equally amongst all hands – providing I get your full cooperation.'

He returned to the quarter-deck, Mr Standish hurrying to keep pace with him. The young man was in a state of rare excitement. He knew of the airships though had never seen one, and it was thrilling to have rescued one of their crew – a man who would have marvellous stories to tell of steering with all sails unfurled through pinnacles and canyons of cloud.

He said anxiously, trotting along, 'Is it possible, do you think, that the airship is still afloat?'

Kristiensen halted at the entrance to the companion-way. He looked slowly over his shoulder and shook his head.

Mr Standish followed him down the steps to the narrow passage. 'The craft he was in stayed afloat, so perhaps the airship did too.'

'Not possible,' Kristiensen said. He opened the door to his cabin and went swiftly round the chart-table to a cupboard in the corner, unlocking it with a small silver key he took from his pocket.

'You sound very certain.'

'Shut the door.' Kristiensen began to take medical supplies from the cupboard: phials of coloured liquids, tubes containing emollients, bandages, salt tablets, and various other preparations. He glanced up and said in a flat expressionless voice: 'I'm certain the airship isn't still afloat because there *is* no airship.'

The First Mate smiled apologetically. 'You mean the airship has been lost? I'm sorry, I don't—'

'I mean that there is no airship,' Kristiensen said distinctly. 'There never was.'

'He isn't from an airship?'

'No.'

The First Mate regarded him blankly.

'I had to spin the crew a tale to calm them down. It wouldn't take much just now to panic them. But he's no more from an airship than you or I. I've seen the uniforms they wear, and this man belongs to no service that I'm familiar with.'

'But we found him in the middle of the ocean. He's not from a sailing vessel, that much is clear, so what other explanation is there?'

'I don't know,' the Captain said thoughtfully. He placed the supplies in a small canvas bag and handed it to the First Mate. 'But I suggest we find out as quickly as possible.'

They found Mr Swann and several of the men clustered round the bunk in which the man lay, still attired in the one-piece garment and showing no signs of recovery. The Second Mate moved aside to allow Kristiensen access, saying, 'His breathing is shallow but I don't think he's injured in any way. There are no wounds or bruising that I can see.'

'His skin,' Mr Standish said. 'It's so white.' He couldn't yet fully take in what the Captain had told him: that here was someone who had appeared as if by magic from nowhere. But of course there had to be a sensible, rational explanation. No educated person, especially in this advanced age, believed for a moment in the inexplicable, the extra-ordinary. There was always a reason to explain everything, from the behaviour of people to those events which at first seemed to defy common sense. For those who didn't conform to this belief there was the inescapable reality of Psy-Con, which no one in his right mind would deny.

Kristiensen told the crew members to clear out of the way,

and it seemed for a moment as if the Summarian might object, but then Mr Swann made a gesture which was unambiguous in its intention. He closed the cabin door firmly behind them and stood with his back to it.

Kristiensen leaned over the unconscious man and carefully cut the material away with his knife until he was naked to the waist. His flesh seemed to glow, as if illuminated from within; and Mr Standish, his eyes straining in the dim light, started involuntarily and said, 'You can see his bones.'

'And also his blood vessels,' the Captain added.

Indeed it was true: the man was translucent. His flesh was solid enough to the touch and yet it was possible to see below the surface, to see actually inside him – the vague milky outline of the skeleton and musculature, the tenuous network of arteries and veins, the shadowy bulk of the inner organs, like pebbles seen darkly at the bottom of a murky pool. And there was something else. Kristiensen touched the man's left shoulder and traced the shape that was imprinted there, as though branded into the flesh. It was a circle with a bar set diagonally through the lower right-hand arc. It was the letter Q.

The First Mate said wonderingly, 'Is he a man? Is he human?'

'He's a man all right,' Kristiensen replied. 'Though where he comes from and to what race he belongs I haven't a notion. Mr Swann, what do you make of this?'

The Second Mate stepped forward, his dark square face sober and perplexed. He gazed his fill at the figure on the bunk, and then his brows grew close together; his arms hung by his sides, impotent, urging some kind of action. He looked towards the Captain as if seeking some friendly reassurance, a sensible and rational explanation.

Kristiensen held a tube to each of the man's nostrils and squirted something inside which dispersed like mist in the nasal cavity. They waited for a moment but there was no response.

'What does the mark on his shoulder signify?' Mr Standish asked.

'It's not a birthmark, at least I don't think so,' Mr Swann said. 'It's too exact and well-formed.'

'A badge of rank perhaps,' Kristiensen said, which was less a query than an inward musing.

'But where is he *from*?' Mr Standish said. 'A man adrift on the ocean must come from somewhere.' He looked at the others; for some reason he felt light-headed and was aware of a trembling in his fingertips. There was no threat of danger, so why should he feel so odd? The mystery of it deepened his anxiety.

The Captain spread an emollient preparation over the man's chest and shoulders and smoothed it into the skin. His large broad hands had a surprising delicacy of touch. He took a strip of cloth from a bottle containing a pale amber liquid and placed it underneath the man's left armpit. After a second or two he removed the strip and examined it; Mr Standish noticed that it had changed colour, from dark red to pink.

'His body temperature is normal,' Kristiensen said. 'There's little we can do for him except keep him under observation, above all keep his temperature down, and immediately he shows signs of recovery—'

'Captain!' Mr Swann said. He stumbled forward.

The man's eyelids were flickering. A muscle moved in his shoulder and a spasm of nervous energy contracted the muscles of his chest. His lips trembled and tried to form themselves into a word. The First Mate experienced a sudden cold prickling down his spine and his mouth was hot and parched.

Kristiensen was straining to hear what the man was trying to say. The words, when they came, were mingled with his breath, barely above a whisper.

'What is it? What does he say?' asked Mr Swann.

The Captain straightened up, the lines like furrows on his forehead. 'It's difficult to make out. He keeps repeating the same words, something that sounds like "Time no longer" or "Will be time no longer". Does that make sense to anyone?'

The Second Mate said grimly, 'I wouldn't expect it to make sense, not coming from him. He's a queer cove, as is obvious to anyone with eyes in his head.'

'Will he be all right?' Mr Standish asked.

'I believe so.' Kristiensen stood up to his full height, his head almost touching the beams. 'We must let him rest, then feed him as soon as he's conscious. Mr Swann, is there a man you can trust to keep watch over him? We need someone of a calm disposition who can keep his mouth shut and not blab to the rest of the crew. Any more shocks or surprises and we'll have a mutiny on our hands.' He stepped into the passage, the First Mate close behind, and they returned to the Captain's quarters.

There was an atmosphere aboard the barque that night that was almost tangible: a presence pervading everywhere, above and below deck. The air was sultry, the vessel drifting languidly beneath the canopy of stars on its silent lonely course; behind it the knife-edge track of bubbling phosphorescence stretching like a slug's trail to the black horizon.

Kristiensen found sleep impossible. He tried to read a book which dealt with the origin and meaning of ancient symbols – hoping to find and identify the mark imprinted on the man's shoulder – but his concentration kept sliding off the page, and after a while he snapped the book shut and went up to the quarter-deck where Mr Swann was taking the second watch. Because of the presence of the man at the wheel they talked of inconsequential matters, avoiding any mention of the stranger and striving to keep their voices calm and unconcerned. From deep below, within the bowels of the ship, there came now and then the sharp crack of a whiplash followed by a dull murmur of dark voices which gradually faded into the night; nothing else disturbed the calm.

Towards dawn, with the vessel still asleep it seemed, the seaman whom Mr Swann had chosen to keep watch over the stranger – he was a boy of eighteen – appeared on deck and ran like a shadow to the companion-ladder, calling for the Second Mate to come quickly. Kristiensen stepped to the forward rail and demanded sharply to know what was the matter. The boy came up on to the quarter-deck, his sunburnt face almost invisible in the darkness and his bleached hair gleaming like a cap of silver.

'They're in the cabin, I couldn't stop them.' The boy was gasping and visibly trembling. 'They said he had a curse upon him and would make the ship founder. I could do nothing, they—'

'How many of them?' Kristiensen said crisply.

'Four, five, I'm not sure. The Summarian said—'

'I might have known he'd have a hand in this; the others wouldn't have had the nerve on their own. What was it he said?'

'He – he said,' the boy stuttered. 'He said the man, the stranger, had the mark of the beast upon him. He said the brand on his shoulder was the sign of the Evil Eye and that we would all perish if he wasn't cast back into the sea.'

The Second Mate spoke urgently in the Captain's ear. 'Mr Standish has the cabin adjoining. Do you think he's safe?'

'He has a pistol, he should be able to defend himself if necessary. But we must hurry if we're to save the stranger from harm.' Kristiensen addressed the boy: 'Can you handle a flintlock?'

'I think so. Yes, sir.'

'Good lad. Mr Swann, break out the arms locker in my cabin, two flintlocks apiece. We must check this before it erupts into open mutiny.' As he spoke the first rays of morning light began to streak the southern sky. The ocean was a dark sluggish mass of purple under the fading stars. Once again it was going to be a day of stifling heat and humidity, the slack breeze barely filling the yellow sails.

The Second Mate returned with the flintlock pistols, loaded and primed, and Kristiensen led the way down the companion-ladder and across the deck. There was no sound from below. The Summarian and his fellow conspirators were moving with the stealth and cunning of bilge rats, down there in the creaking passageways and shadowed cabins. For such a big man Kristiensen was light as a cat on his feet, creeping down the ladders below decks with Mr Swann close behind and the boy nervously bringing up the rear. Approaching the cabin they heard ('Ssshhhh!' Kristiensen said) the muffled sound of voices; and then all at once, in the near blackness, very close to them, something moved – what Kristiensen instantly took to be the look-out posted by the Summarian – and raised his pistol, cocked the hammer, and shot Mr Standish straight through the

25

head. The young man gave no cry, made no sound, but fell immediately to the floor, all life extinguished from his body. The lead ball had split his skull in two like a pomegranate and the contents were stuck to the walls and bulkhead.

Kristiensen stepped over the remains and rapped with the butt of his pistol on the cabin door. There was no sound or movement from within. He gestured to the Second Mate and the boy to take up positions on either side of the door and then called out:

'This is the Captain. No harm will befall you if you lay down your arms and open the door. But if you resist I shall slaughter you to a man, without hesitation or mercy. You know I am a man of my word.'

There was a movement behind the door, and then: 'You are forgetting, Captain, that we have the hostage.' It was, unmistakably, the wheedling nasal croak of the Summarian.

'The stranger means nothing to me,' Kristiensen replied. 'It is the safety of the ship which is my chief concern.' He winked at Mr Swann. 'Will you obey the order or shall I use force?'

'One moment, Captain.'

There came the sound of rapid, muttered conversation and the occasional oath or two, then eventually the Summarian's: 'The game is not worth the candle. We have your word? Is it a bargain that we shall receive no punishment?'

Kristiensen smiled but his voice was without humour. 'Absolutely. You have my word.'

A bolt was drawn back and the door opened to reveal, in the dim yellow light of a smoking oil-lamp, the slitted wary eyes of the Summarian peering from an olive countenance and behind him the fearful expression of three members of the crew – all four holding an assortment of weapons and semi-poised in the shadows, prepared to fight if need be, yet none of them so keen as to make a premature move.

Beyond them, glowing like a pale ghostly incubus, Kristiensen could see the figure of the stranger in the bunk; the Captain stared and it was all he could manage not to utter a cry of amazement: the stranger's eyes were open and he appeared to be fully conscious. And even as Kristiensen watched, the

stranger's hands gripped the sides of the bunk and he began to
rise up into a vertical position, whereupon the Summarian and
his fellow conspirators, following the Captain's gaze, dropped
their weapons and fell to their knees, a babble of craven sup-
plication and incoherent fear on their lips.

The day, as Kristiensen had expected, was heavy and lethargic.
The barque moved fitfully through the low waves, occasionally
throwing up a spumed peak of pinkish froth which glistened
against the black tar-coated timbers above which the unicorn's
horn of the prow pointed unchangingly towards New Amerika.

It seemed to Kristiensen – as it always did at this point –
that this was a voyage without end. Perhaps there would actually come a time when they wouldn't sight land, when the look-
out in the crow's nest would strain his eyes day after day,
searching the horizon in vain for the thin hazy sliver signifying
journey's end. But meanwhile his charts reassured him that
within twelve hours, twenty-four at the most, they would be
leaving the doldrums and picking up the northward-sweeping
currents of the Main. Then it would be plain sailing into the
Bay of Granada and past the clusters of tropical islands which
comprised the Granadian Chain.

It was at midday, the sun almost directly overhead, that the
sloop – fore-and-aft rigged for speed – was sighted, approaching from the south-west. Even before it was close enough
to be identified, Kristiensen and the Second Mate exchanged
glances of foreboding; it was unlikely to be a King's frigate in
this latitude, and even less likely a merchantman. There remained only one possibility, which as the vessel gained on them
during the next hour transpired to be the possibility they most
dreaded. It was a pirate ship.

The Captain appraised it through the telescope, noting the
massed cannon, the battering-ram prow reinforced with iron
rivets, the crude skull-and-crossbones flag fluttering limply at
the mast. Immediately he instructed that a telegraph message
be sent to the mainland (they were now within range of the
coastal receiving stations) asking for assistance from the Royal
Naval Fleet, though the likelihood of a vessel being anywhere

27

in the vicinity was extremely small. But it was their only hope, for they hadn't the remotest chance of outrunning a sloop rigged for speed on the high seas.

She bore down on them steadily at eight or nine knots, the scarlet bow-wave aimed unerringly to intercept their course within the hour. The pirates would have no compunction about the wholesale slaughter of Captain and crew, for the cargo in the lower holds was far too valuable to allow the maudlin diversion of a few petty scruples. On the open market each of the three hundred human souls would fetch anything from five to ten Spanish gold dollars, depending on condition, and anything dead would be sold as protein supplement for the slaves already in captivity. The edict of King Jimmy K to limit the number of slaves brought into the country (for fear of over-supply which would depress market values) had not yet come into force, and the traders were scrambling over themselves to fill their pens before the official quotas became law.

Mr Swann reported that the message had been sent and an acknowledgment received, though no promise of aid had been given. Kristiensen knew that it would require a minor miracle to avert what seemed an inevitable and inescapable fate, and as the pirate vessel came within cannon-range he prepared himself for the warning shot across his bows. The two vessels were now maintaining a parallel course, with the pirate ship closing minute by minute; then Kristiensen became aware of something he couldn't account for. He glanced across at the Second Mate, and he too was looking puzzled. It seemed – though at first Kristiensen doubted the evidence of his own eyes – that the *Slave Trader* was actually pulling away and, inconceivably, the gap between the two ships was widening. But why should this be? Kristiensen wondered. The pirate vessel was falling away astern, the distance between them increasing all the while, and yet the sails of his own vessel were flapping tiredly in the stale air, providing the barque with hardly enough power to outpace a longboat.

'Damn, but that's the queerest thing!' Kristiensen exclaimed. 'How do you account for it?' he asked Mr Swann, who was not looking at the pirate ship but gazing down on the main deck.

Kristiensen turned his attention there too, and standing at the rail, observing the receding vessel with perfectly calm detachment, was the tall figure of the stranger, the skin of his bare torso as pale as alabaster.

The Experiment

Dr Mathew Black took the Greencab downtown and hopped out on the corner of Third Avenue and East 14th, opposite the impressive granite bulk of the Franko Foundation building. He was late; it seemed that nowadays he could do nothing to schedule, from eating breakfast to making love: time escaped as through a sieve and he was always in a hurry to catch up with yesterday. And now the MDA (Medikal Direktorate Authority), not content with restricting his budget for the new fiscal year, had increased his workload with yet another priority case for which they required immediate answers and snap judgments. If only he had the staff, resources and equipment then maybe he could have gone half-way to meeting their demands, but they were expecting the impossible when all he had to offer was the merely adequate.

The new blonde receptionist smiled her most fetching grimace and he mentally filed her away under Desirability +7, Availability +9. Perhaps dinner in a quiet restaurant, a couple of highballs, and the suggestion of a nightcap in his bachelor apartment . . . but in the meantime he had enough on his plate, sex aside, to fill most of his waking hours. So he adopted his professional manner and asked for the Admissions Sheet, which she placed before him on the grey vinyl-topped counter. There were three entries: two private patients who were in for routine checks and the third with the ominous words 'MDA Referral' printed alongside. Black noted that the patient had already been placed in isolation, which was standard procedure for any admission without a previous medikal record.

He handed the clipboard to the receptionist and said, 'Is

anyone attending to the MDA case?' He had a slight lisp which many of the female staff found rather attractive.

'Dr Hallam,' the blonde receptionist said. 'You weren't here and so—'

'I didn't ask for an autopsy, Miss—'

'Jardine,' the girl said, a little breathlessly.

'Miss Jardine. I wasn't here because I was stuck in the cogging traffic, which as you'll appreciate is pretty heavy at this time of day.'

'I quite understand,' Miss Jardine said.

'Good. I think we're going to get along.'

'I do hope so,' Miss Jardine breathed.

Black smiled to show he was master of the situation, and went on his way. He was conscious of being watched, and as always wished he had an extra couple of inches to add to his less than adequate five feet four.

Dr Hallam looked up as he came into the isolation room with its metal bed and leather straps and the two tall cabinets filled with apparatus. There was the faint smell of preserving fluid.

'You didn't waste any time, I see,' Black said, taking down a rubber apron and putting it on over his street-clothes.

'I did wait,' Dr Hallam said, almost primly. 'The case is urgent and I thought under the circumstances it would be wise to proceed without delay.'

'Very correct,' Black said dryly. 'As usual,' he added, glancing at the patient. The sight of the man lying on the metal bed startled him; he seemed to be transparent. 'Have you carried out any tests?'

'In accordance with standard procedure I bled him first.' Dr Hallam nodded towards three bloated leeches floating in a bell-jar containing a colourless fluid.

'I shouldn't have thought there was anything to bleed,' Black said lightly.

'There wasn't. Whatever that stuff is in his veins, it isn't blood. It might even be toxic because, you may have noticed, the leeches are dead.'

Black moved towards the patient with a certain amount of

31

caution. 'Have you tested for typhus, cholera, bubonic plague? We don't want a widespread epidemic on our hands.' There was still the fear amongst the urban population of New Amerika that one of the unconquered diseases might suddenly flare up and decimate an entire city. It had happened in 18.14, in 18.29, and even now – in 18.40 – the most allusive rumour was enough to make front-page headlines and panic whole communities into evacuating the cities and heading westwards towards the scattered pioneer settlements of the lowland plains.

'Negative on all counts,' Dr Hallam said.

Black touched the patient's arm. 'This is an interesting condition. Did the MDA say what they hoped to learn about him?'

'Not specifically; they'd like a full report prior to deportation. But as he came off a slave ship they're worried about him being a possible plague-carrier.'

'He's to be deported?' Black said. 'They've already decided that he's to receive treatment?'

Dr Hallam faced him across the bed, smiling faintly and without warmth. 'You know as well as I do, Mathew, that "treatment" is the last thing he'll receive in Psy-Con. It's a pity we can't keep him here under observation for a while; he could prove very useful in our research program. Perhaps the stuff in his bloodstream has a high immunity factor against disease, something we could isolate and use as a preventative.'

Black nodded thoughtfully. Tentatively he touched the man's left shoulder and asked, 'Why was he branded? It looks like an old burn that's healed up.'

'Nobody seems to know. He was like that when they found him.'

'And why the Q shape? It must have some significance. Is it a slave brand, do you think?'

'I've checked the records and there's nothing listed using that symbol as a means of identification. He was picked up in the ocean, and that's as much as anyone knows about him.'

Black felt for the man's pulse. 'How long has he been unconscious?'

'He was like this when they admitted him early this morning. I assume he was put under heavy sedation by the Authority mediks, though there's nothing in the file. Do you think he might be violent?'

'Let's bring him round. We'll try pins in the soles of his feet.'

Dr Hallam was averse to the practice but it was standard procedure in bringing someone round; after several pins had been inserted into his flesh the patient showed signs of returning consciousness; he opened his eyes and the first word he uttered was 'Ouch.'

'Normal response,' Black remarked. 'That's encouraging.' He made sure that the straps securing the man's wrists were as tight as possible and then leaned over the bed so that he was in his line of vision. The patient's eyes were open, though hazy and unfocused. For some reason they made Black feel uncomfortable, as though he wasn't there, the eyes looking right through him.

'Can you hear me? Do you understand me?'

The man said, 'I've got pins and needles in my feet.'

Dr Hallam laughed. 'I'll say you have.'

'At least he understands Spanish.' Black began to question the patient but the answers weren't at all satisfactory. He seemed to have no memory at all of the past, couldn't tell them who he was or where he had come from, and had no idea of how he had found himself in the middle of the ocean. The odd thing was that he didn't appear curious or perturbed that he couldn't remember anything. Altogether it was very strange.

'Well,' Black said finally, 'at least you're conscious, which is some sort of progress.' He said slowly and clearly, 'Do you know what's going to happen to you? Do you know that the Authority have made arrangements for your deportation?'

The patient's eyes hardened into focus and he looked at Black for the first time. 'The Authority?'

'The MDA. They've sent you here for preliminary tests, but afterwards you're to be committed to Psy-Con.'

Dr Hallam cast a warning glance at Black; he received the message and nodded to show that he understood. Patients sometimes reacted violently or went into seizure when informed what was to happen to them. They were already emotionally disturbed and it served no purpose to alarm them unnecessarily.

But the man said calmly, 'Whatever happens will happen. There is nothing any of us can do to alter the prearranged pattern.' He tried to move and realized he was strapped down. He showed surprise.

'Standard procedure,' Black and Dr Hallam said together, and laughed.

'I see.' The man seemed to understand perfectly. He was unlike any patient Black had dealt with before: he was odd, no question about it, but didn't exhibit the usual signs of madness. Most patients had a cock-eyed view of the world and found it difficult to accept society as it was and to live by the rules as laid down under Royal Charter. Some of them thought the whole thing a fake, an elaborate confidence-trick with the MDA the arch-villain: they even accused Black of being part of the subterfuge, implying that it was they who inhabited the real world while he lived in a dream. The problem was in making them see the error of their ways, in pointing out that the only alternative to a full and normal life was Psy-Con, the mere thought of which was enough to give anyone the willies.

Black said that he wished to speak to Dr Hallam in private. They walked slowly along the corridor to Black's office.

'How do you think the Authority would regard an application for deferment?' He spoke as if the thought was still germinating in his mind. 'We could learn a great deal here—'

He checked himself as a group of men in black marched past, the tramp of boots loud and echoing. There was somebody dressed in white with bare feet among them.

Dr Hallam opened the door of Black's office. 'On what grounds? He's free of any disease, negative on all counts. We have no medikal right to hold him, once a deportation order has been issued. I don't see why I should stick my neck out for the sake of a loonie.'

Black went to the window and stared out for a moment. Then he turned abruptly. 'We could say that the skin condition is causing us some concern, that we want to try some compounds on it, sulphuric or something. Couldn't we say that?'

34

His lisp became more pronounced as his voice quickened with excitement. 'We've carried out the standard tests, fine, and there's been negative reaction, but *we're* the experts on contagious diseases, not the Authority. We could say in the report' – he waved his hands seeking suitable phrases – 'we could recommend long-term observation. Perhaps there's a virus we're unfamiliar with, related to the skin condition, who's to know? We want to keep him here just to make sure.'

'Better safe than sorry.'

'Exactly.' Black rubbed his hands together. Dr Hallam hadn't seen him so worked up for some time.

'And if the Authority agrees, what then?'

'Gestalt Treatment.'

'But it hasn't been approved,' Dr Hallam said, alarmed. 'We don't know what effect it might have.'

'That's why we should try it *now*,' Black said eagerly. 'I've been dying to have a go for ages, what better opportunity? We have a guinea-pig ready and waiting and strapped down. Who knows what we might learn about how the Treatment works? It could be a breakthrough.'

'It might kill him. Have you thought of that?'

'There are always risks in any experiment,' Black conceded. 'In any case a post-mortem would be almost as valuable; and just think of the prestige if we succeed!'

Dr Hallam went to the window and gazed silently into nothingness, then looked directly at Black. 'Do we have the necessary equipment?'

'We have a galvanoscope which Benson was using for the separation of alkaline solutions. He's being transferred to the King's Commission, so he won't miss it. And it shouldn't be beyond us to rig up a galvanic battery and belt.' He gripped Dr Hallam's arm. 'What do you say? Is it worth a try?' His hand moved downwards and gripped Dr Hallam's left buttock. There was a wicked gleam in his eye.

Dr Hallam shuddered. 'You always know the best way to get round me. I should say no—'

'But you won't,' said Black, his other hand unfastening the buttons on the white coat and slipping inside.

'Oh Mathew—' Dr Hallam's lips were red and moist and yielding. Black pushed her on to the desk and opened her legs with his knee and standing between them inserted himself with a quick stab. She moaned and gripped his shoulders.

'You'll help me, Sarah, won't you?' Black was thrusting in and out. 'We'll wire him up together, you and I, and give him the Treatment.'

'Yes, Mathew, yes.' Her voice was shaking with the movement and her own emotion. 'You won't be unfaithful to me?'

'What put that idea into your head?' Black said, panting like a dog.

'The new blonde girl on Reception is very attractive. I thought you might fancy—'

'Forget it,' said Black, grunting. 'All I'm interested in is medikal science.'

Permission was granted for a period of deferment, though it was made clear that responsibility for the patient rested entirely with Doktors Black and Hallam. The few days during which the equipment was being assembled and set up were actually pleasant for the man in isolation – being unaware of the forthcoming treatment he was able to relax, to regain his strength, under the impression that once the 'tests' were completed he would be moved to another wing of the sanatorium. Black became quite friendly, dropping in at various times during the day and bringing him reading material. The man known as Q seemed to have a vacuum inside his head which was ready to be filled with whatever was to hand. Black brought him Packshape's *The Tailor of Valencia*, which Q much enjoyed; he particularly liked the scene where the young female advocate, masquerading as a man, resorts to a striptease in order to disconcert the prosecuting counsel and so win the case.

Dr Hallam was less comfortable in the presence of Q. It was something she couldn't articulate but which, nonetheless, she could almost feel as a tangible aura: not unpleasant exactly, just inexplicable. On one occasion he asked about the relationship between herself and Dr Black, and when she replied that they were professional colleagues and nothing more he looked at her sceptically and said, 'I see you both as a single entity, as two halves of the same person.' He regarded her with large soft grey eyes, the colour of a winter sky, and it seemed to Sarah that he must know many things, and yet he professed to remember nothing.

She said to him: 'You have no past, not even a name. You're curious about the world but not about yourself, where you came from, how you happen to be here.'

'The world is nothing until we think of it in a certain way,' Q said. 'It doesn't exist as objective reality, only as a subjective perception.'

Sarah was upset by this. 'I don't understand,' she said, intimidated by his knowingness. 'Do you mean to say that nothing exists, that people don't exist?'

'Not separately of perception,' he answered. 'Would the reflection of the moon in a pool of water exist if there was no one to look at it?'

'Why . . . yes . . .' She was confused. 'I think so. We know that the moon is there, we can see it, and the pool of water is there.'

'And the reflection?' Q said. 'When you move, it moves too. Where is it any one moment?' He opened his hands, his wrists still bound to the metal frame of the bed.

Sarah laughed, not very convincingly. 'And what does that prove?'

'It proves that we each exist through the perceptions of others. You live in my brain. Why is it that Dr Blake—'

'Black,' she corrected him.

'Black: of course. I must try to remember. Why is it that he denies the existence of the seven senses? I read somewhere that radiovision is being developed, which means you must have knowledge of electromagnetism. You might even know of the EMI Field, though I haven't seen a reference to it.'

'This is subversive talk, I refuse to listen,' Sarah said abruptly. 'Every sane person knows there are only six senses, the rest are aberrations.'

Q was unperturbed. 'Name them.'

37

She looked at him defiantly and rattled them off. 'Touch, taste, sight, smell, hearing, sex.'

'At least two of those are electromagnetic in source. The sense you omitted—'

'I will report this conversation to the Authority,' she said harshly. 'There are worse things than deportation, believe me.' Her cheeks were flushed and her eyes hard and bright. 'Everything you say is pure delusion.'

She stood up. Then it was true: the man was fit only for Psy-Con. For a while she had been deceived into thinking of him as a normal, rational being, but now there was no doubt that his mind was unhinged. She removed the book he had been reading (Disraeli's *Presidential Days*) and for good measure tightened the straps another final notch. Mathew had been so right about him – to suggest that human brains were responsible for creating the world when it was evident that reality was all around – in her own warm body and the hard wooden floor and the sound of boots marching along the corridor . . .

But she had to get out. She was suffocating. The room was oppressing her with its heavy, cloying stench. It was only outside – when steadying her breathing and feeling her knees to be filled with water – that she realized the root of her panic: she had been sexually approached by him and had, almost without realizing, responded. The bond had been made and she was as weak and as wet as a new-born babe.

Alone in the room Q closed his eyes and entered the continuing dream of another time and place; his limbs were trembling and saliva was forming thickly in his mouth. In this dream he sees black fathomless spaces, without stars or the faintest light, in which the laws of the natural world have no meaning. The world he inhabits is an arbitrary place in space and time. Within him he feels the urging of a greater knowledge, as of a pattern forming through mist, dimly perceived, the blurred image hardening into definition. And the straps holding him to the metal bed dissolve and his body rises up and floats unhindered above the city, higher still into vacuum; and he is bathed in the cold pure light of a million galaxies.

Dr Mathew Black was bent on achieving success: nothing would deflect him from the course he had single-mindedly envisioned for himself. He would become known as the foremost practitioner of the technique known as Gestalt Treatment. It had yet to be decided what was its precise function and purpose; nobody was absolutely sure. In 18.19 a young scientist, Pierre Boorman, working in the specialized sub-field of genetic heritage, had accidentally discovered that a paralytic tension could be induced in living tissue by the action of certain chemicals. The apparatus he devised – the galvanic battery and pile – became the basis for a new experimental branch of physiological science known as galvanology, and Boorman the very first galvanologist. As with most discoveries it was, in the beginning, an interesting phenomenon but lacked a medikal application, and it wasn't till the 18.30s, when the Gestalt Proposition was formulated, that research workers began to see how galvanology could be applied to obtain valid and useful data. Not a great deal of work had been done since then, and the results so far had been patchy and inconclusive. The theory – the idea – was that by attaching patients to the apparatus (the galvanic belt) it would be possible to purge them of all non-associative thoughts. Healthy human beings, as everyone knew, conformed to a strict pattern of behaviour without any deviation from the norm, whereas those who were ill were afflicted by random notions ('imaginative leaps' was the medikal term) which made them behave in strange and unpredictable ways. Rid them of these non-associative thoughts, the theory went, and you would have healthy, happy human beings in place of the thousands deported each year to Psy-Con. Whether Gestalt Treatment was the answer, or even a workable alternative, nobody knew; Dr Mathew Black, at the frontier of medikal knowledge, was one of those determined to find out. And not only would it be a tremendous leap forward, it would also make his reputation and assure him of a long and distinguished career.

At the moment, however, there was need for secrecy, and Black had to proceed circumspectly; the Authority must be presented with a *fait accompli* – positive and conclusive evidence that the technique was viable and would produce the desired effect. In his office he had over the previous months assembled a small library pertinent to galvanology and the theories relating to Gestalt Treatment. He had already coined the phrase 'Black's Procedure', and in his mind's eye could see it emblazoned in Gothik script on the title page of the treatise he would have the proud pleasure of presenting at the MDA Annual Conference. No one, not even Sarah, knew of this. Subversion and treachery were everywhere; one's colleagues especially were not to be trusted. Give that idiot Benson a whiff and he'd poke his long beaky nose in.

On the morning of the day chosen for the experiment, Black and Sarah Hallam sat in his office working out the final details. The rats had been busy during the night and the papers on the desk were littered and smeared with droppings. There were two packs which roamed the sanatorium, one black, one grey, continually at war over which should have the choice bits of dead flesh in the disposal chutes in the sluice rooms; the greys were in the ascendancy, their fat sleek bodies rustling behind cabinets and their high-pitched squeaks plainly audible as they fought the blacks for a tasty tit-bit.

'It's time the Authority did something about this,' Black said angrily, picking up each piece of paper and shaking it. 'All this might have been ruined. How am I expected to work?'

'You should consider yourself fortunate.' Sarah took a handkerchief from her white coat and rubbed the desk. 'Penney came in one day last week and found half of one of his patients gone.'

'Which half?' Black asked with a sly grin.

'The legs and feet.'

'At least he had something left to work with,' Black said, and his humour was so infectious that she couldn't help smiling. That was one of the reasons, Sarah realized, why she loved him so much. The others in the sanatorium were such dull, featureless people. She lifted her head at the sound of tramping boots: another deportee on his last journey. She had never visited Psy-Con, though Black had promised to include her name on the rota of visiting medikal staff; he himself went there twice a year on regular tours of inspection.

He said, 'Do you feel confident you can handle the battery? The amount of current applied is most important. We don't want to kill him right off. Keep within the limits and watch for fluctuations in the current. Benson warned me that a sudden increase in the charge can cause permanent damage.'

'You've mentioned the experiment to him?' Sarah said, her eyes widening.

'I said we were carrying out a routine test. He doesn't know we have a guinea-pig.'

'How do we know the amount of charge the patient can withstand? Surely it will vary.'

'There are two conditions to watch out for,' Black said, wiping the seat and sitting down. 'Eyeball retraction and the erection quotient. The eyeballs retract and roll upwards so that only the whites remain visible, and the patient – providing he's a man, of course – exhibits an erection which increases with the amount of charge applied. When he's fully extended we're roughly at the limit of tolerance, so you'll have to keep your eye on it and judge when he's had enough.'

Sarah nodded and looked down at the papers on the desk. She tried to give the impression of not breathing.

Black said: 'Think you can handle it?'

'I'll do my best.'

'Good girl.' He held up his two clenched fists. 'Think what this could mean! We could be on the verge of a radical new departure that will make Gestalt Treatment and galvanology standard procedure throughout the country. Aren't you excited?' He was like a child about to open a Christmas present, his eyes agleam, his hands fluttering.

Sarah smiled. She was restless herself. 'What results are we looking for? Will there be actual signs of purging or will it be an interior process? I find it hard to visualize exactly what will happen.'

'That's going to be the interesting part – seeing precisely how it works and what effect it has. I should imagine there will be a good deal of pain and perhaps the patient will bleed, vomit and have diarrhoea. But almost certainly there's going to be an outpouring of non-associative thoughts, a stream of random and meaningless gabble.'

'Not very pleasant to watch,' Sarah commented.

'No, perhaps not,' Black agreed. 'But vitally interesting, all the same. He'll empty the contents of his mind and rid himself of all the crazy notions which get in the way of rational thinking and acceptable social behaviour. It's going to be thrilling.'

'Yes,' Sarah said, her mind conjuring up visions – quite inexplicably – of the erection quotient. 'I think you're right.'

The apparatus was less complicated than she had feared, consisting of a galvanic battery connected by wires to a galvanic belt, which was simply a strip of leather with metal studs inserted into it: the belt fastened round the patient's chest over the heart and was tightened so that all the studs were impressed into the body. The other piece of equipment was the galvanoscope – a small square box with knobs and dials – used for detecting and indicating the direction of the electric charge.

Q submitted passively to the fitting of the belt, not at all concerned by the clutter of equipment and the wires strung across the room. Black explained perfunctorily that it was a standard test and there was no need to worry: everybody had it done. Sarah folded back the bedclothes to reveal the pale translucent body, her eyes delicately avoiding that part of the patient's body which was an integral part of the experiment. Instead she busied herself with adjusting the belt and making sure the terminals were greased and properly connected.

Black switched on the galvanoscope and a faint crackling came from the battery and the acrid smell of chemicals, pungent to the nostrils. The needle on the dial flickered into life as the charge built up.

'Response?' Black said. He was watching the dial.

'Negative.' Sarah glanced swiftly at the patient and away again.

Black adjusted the controls and the needle rose steadily, the crackling sound becoming louder. A puff of blue smoke drifted from the battery. The patient's left foot twitched and the muscles in his arms went rigid; he made a noise in his throat and his eyeballs rolled upward.

'Response?'

Sarah looked and saw that he was reacting. She thought: My God, is he reacting! Her chest expanded and it was as though she couldn't get enough air to enter her lungs. She felt most peculiar. Now she couldn't take her eyes off him, watching almost in a trance as the various parts of his body twitched and jerked and his mouth now clamped shut and now gaped in a dry gasp of pain. The erection quotient dragged her back to reality, making it plain that he was reaching the limit of tolerance.

'Hold it there, that's enough, he's responding.'

'Good,' Black said. 'Excellent.' His eyes were alive. 'It's damn well working! The damn thing is working!'

The patient's eyes were wide and blank, without pupils, and his jaw began to jerk mechanically. A babble of something came out, mingled with the foam on his lips, and then he began to talk, purging himself of all random, non-associative thoughts.

3

The Dream Tape

"Of the one hundred thousand million stars in the Milky Way it had been estimated by statistical computation that upwards of eighty-three per cent possessed one or more planetary bodies of sufficient mass to enable them to retain an atmosphere. Many of these were extremely massive by Old Earth standards, and it was thought that their tremendous surface gravity would have subverted the conditions necessary for the creation of life: the basic carbon components could not have progressed beyond the most elementary stages of molecular manufacture and duplication. The number of system-containing planets with a suitable atmosphere for the creation of life at zero point in spacetime (ie: within a span of 10,000 years before and after the present moment) was close to 10^8, or one hundred million. This meant that within the Milky Way galaxy there were 100,000,000 planets capable of supporting life – in however bizarre a form that might be.

Extending this hypothesis to the limits of the observable Metagalaxy (the Hubble Radius of 1.3×10^{10} light-years, or 13,000 million light-years) there were an estimated 3,000,000,000 galaxies each containing an average of 100,000,000,000 stars. If every hundredth star had a solar system with just one habitable planet, the observable Metagalaxy would contain 3,000,000,000,000,000,000 planets capable of creating and supporting life-forms. Yet so far, in all this vast profusion, not a single humanoid species had been discovered. The age-old question still remained: was man alone in all of Creation?

As a Myth Technologist seeking evidence for the Unified Psychic Field he thought this particularly ironic. To have progressed from Pre-Colonization times when relativistic concepts were being propounded, to have isolated and identified the elementary *quark* sub-microscopic particles which were the basis of energy-matter, to have laid down the principles for the existence of psi phenomena (though not, it had to be admitted, allied them to any of the prime energy sources: electromagnetic, gravitational and nuclear) – to have accomplished all this and still not established that life was or was not a general condition of the Metagalaxy. It seemed almost perverse, as if something unseen had erected a labyrinth of distorting mirrors which constantly hid from view the true nature of reality.

Man was not unique, he would not entertain the notion; besides which he intuitively believed that there had to be intelligent life elsewhere. In a galaxy of one hundred million solar systems with habitable planets, the law of probability indicated that a proportion must have developed or be in the process of developing Phase One, Phase Two or even Phase Three civilizations. Some of these, it was true, would have become biologically unstable and died out; some would have mutated and followed a dead end to extinction or failed to adapt quickly enough to changing conditions; and others would have wiped themselves out, as the human race had been in danger of doing a number of times Pre-Colonization.

And yet it defied every instinct, every one of his senses, to accept the prevailing scientific evidence that intelligent life was nowhere to be found throughout the cosmos except on the nine planetary and five planetoidal states. Man was not alone; nothing would make him believe it.

Christian Queghan had spent the morning in the silent room reading a Paper entitled *Concerning the Hypothesis of Determining Problematical Futures* by Professor Milton Blake. Blake's field of study – MetaPsychical Research – had links with his own subject of Myth Technology, and as Blake was to be one of the guest speakers at the forthcoming Scenario Planning Symposium he had felt duty-bound to read it. Not that this had been a chore: the Paper was concise, cogently argued and introduced a number of concepts worthy of further investigation. The most interesting of these was a technique Blake was pioneering in the Psychic Conservation Unit in which electrical brain impulses could be processed and converted into a three-dimensional visual display. Although still in the experimental stage and technically undervalued (the necessary funds hadn't been allocated to go beyond prototype hardware) there was little doubt in Queghan's mind that it would provide a useful predictive capability.

But now, allowing his concentration to lapse, he was suddenly tired – due not so much to the work, he suspected, as to the indefatigable Castel who had the night before kept him talking into the small hours. Queghan detected within himself a wave of vague irritability and tried to analyse it; was it something innate, a mutual antipathy between them, a fact of body chemistry – or was he simply annoyed at Castel for blathering on about his own specialized field of interest and not once pausing to inquire about his, Queghan's, current preoccupation? Scientists could be petty, jealous people swayed by childish emotions and irrelevancies, and spiteful too on occasion.

He came out of the MyTT Research annexe. The sun, predictably, was not shining; the forecast had said clear sunny spells and yet the sky was overcast with dank grey cloud. The weather was controlled – in theory at any rate – though Queghan sometimes wondered whether the apparatus was a product of technological innovation or wishful thinking. He was a man of forbidding height, noticably thin, with a face that had been unkindly described as 'cadaverous'; this was too severe and was belied by an expression which softened his features and made him appear almost dreamy. He wore this expression now, of gentle contemplation, as he walked along the gravel path between the neat sprinkled lawns, lost in speculation on Blake's Paper. He had met Blake just once – friendly and alert-faced – at the MyTT Open Science Day when two hundred scientists in related fields had gathered together in a relaxed and informal atmosphere. Yet there had been a more positive and fruitful interchange of views and opinions that day than was possible over six months of communication via official channels.

Approaching the commissary he was struck by the sudden thought that Castel, in his obsessive two-hour monologue, might have been betraying a twinge of professional jealousy. The funds allocated to the TFC Lab had been quadrupled while Castel's request for more money to redeploy the Archives had been politely but resolutely declined. Could that be the reason, Queghan wondered, the doors opening to admit him; maybe Castel was flesh and blood after all and not, as rumour had it, a cyberthetic complex. It was an amusing notion.

Johann Karve, the Director of MyTT, was at the high table with several of his senior research staff. The conversation went on uninterrupted as Queghan took a seat, but he had seen the Director's brief passing glance and almost imperceptible nod of greeting. Johann was adept at keeping everyone on a happy equilibrium, counterbalancing the excesses of personality, one against the other. Some thought him perversely eccentric, almost a dodderer; it was an impression he didn't seek to discourage, but at times to actively foster. As now – nodding gently to a point Brenton was making with his usual emphatic fervour: the hot-blooded idealist in full flow.

'I doubt whether the Project would significantly benefit,' the Director said when Brenton had finished. 'It would extend it in scope but not in penetration.' He looked in Queghan's direction. 'Does Blake's Paper add to our problems or help solve them, Chris?'

'It's promising,' Queghan replied cautiously. 'Some of his assumptions are shots in the dark, but then whose aren't?'

'Which Paper is this?' Brenton asked quickly, snapping at the bait. Johann Karve's eyes touched Queghan's for a moment, an amused invitation silently acknowledged. Queghan explained briefly some of the ideas the Paper proposed for establishing the existence of – as Blake termed them – 'Problematical Futures' and, if such did exist, how to track, plot and record them. This line of work was parallel with Queghan's research in the TFC Lab, but whereas Milton Blake was investigating the theoretical possibility of alternative futures, the MyTT Research Institute was concerned with exploring them in the real sense: actually injecting someone into a

47

Temporal Flux Centre and (if he wasn't crushed or obliterated in the process) discovering what took place beyond the boundaries of the physical universe, where the laws of space, time and matter were rendered meaningless. The main problem was retrieval. It was very much like, as Director Karve once succinctly remarked, 'A blind man trying to capture a butterfly by reaching barehanded through a compressor blade moving at 15,000 revs a minute'.

There were other difficulties too: how to know precisely where and when and in what alternative future the injectee had landed – mythical or actual? How to communicate with him, and, supposing communication to be possible, how to arrange a specific spacetime coordinate to facilitate retrieval? It was fairly easy to send a man in but would he ever come out again?

Blake's proposal of a mind waves/visual display interface was a promising line of inquiry, for if developed to a sufficiently high degree of technical sophistication it would permit the injectee to transmit images back to the satellite-Control laboratory; and perhaps it might be capable of even more. Queghan could visualize it being used as a predictive facility, whereby the brain patterns of the injectee could be processed to give an accurate and reliable forecast, prior to injection, of the future he was about to enter. Hopefully he would be able to choose any one of a series of multiple universes. This was abstract theory, as Queghan would be the first to admit, and yet on paper it was mathematically feasible; the nuts and bolts of the operation were another matter.

'I should like to see that for myself,' Brenton said. He had a solemn young face with dark hard eyes and a thin mouth which would be reluctant to concede a smile. He was new to the Institute and anxious not to miss out on anything. 'I take it the Paper will be circulated?'

Queghan said, 'Of course,' and looked at Brenton, whose stare was blank, impassive, yet with a touch of veiled insolence. He was on his way to the top and determined to get there by whatever means were to hand. Queghan could have smiled but didn't. He wondered what the young man would find when he got there.

Karve sipped his coffee and mentioned that the newsmedia had been pestering him that morning. 'The two banes of my life,' he said wearily. 'The newsmedia and piles. Both irritatingly painful.' The current rumour said that Project Tempus was reaching the point where it might arouse public interest, especially if a live mission was about to be undertaken. Who was the man, they wanted to know, who was the heroic volunteer about to be launched into the Unknown?

Brenton was alerted. 'Has the selection been made?' he asked the Director.

Johann Karve smiled and stuffed tobacco into his pipe. He possessed an inward stillness, an area of calm, which engendered confidence and trust; his staff were loyal to the degree of religious faith. 'There's a short-list, as you know, Martin. But you have my word that no final decision has been taken. When it is everyone concerned will be notified. We are not a department of the *Polizei*.'

'What did you say to the newsmedia?' Karla Ritblat asked. She was head of the Psycho-Med Faculty whose job it was to prepare the heroic volunteer for injection into the Unknown. The Director, with his aptitude for the deft phrase, had referred to her as 'our chief head-expander'. Karla was forty-six, stiff, unyielding, grey-haired; she had chosen a career in place of child-bearing and had that wary acidic manner which unattractive middle-aged women seem to acquire like defensive armour-plating. She didn't find Karve's description either apposite or amusing, believing that a scientific establishment was no place for levity.

Karve glanced along the table, benign amidst the pipe smoke. 'I issued the routine bulletin. In any case, they're only interested in disaster and catastrophe. Talk to them about the principles of Myth Technology or the theories of Temporal Flux Centres and they assume a staggering indifference.'

'Which is perhaps just as well,' Queghan said. 'If you told them that the world they inhabit is founded on an untenable premise they might really panic. At least before you could explain it in words of one syllable.'

'Is it necessary to be so melodramatic?' Karla Ritblat said, appraising him with her cold, fish-like stare. 'That kind of talk, if heard by outsiders, *does* cause panic.' Queghan wondered, not for the first time, whether Karla had ever considered herself a suitable subject for psycho examination. She would make a most interesting case-study.

'So you think Blake might have something?' Karve said.

'The visual display technique – if it works – would provide the kind of predictive capability we've been looking for. But there is one problem.'

Brenton put his elbows on the table. 'Which is?'

'The brain patterns, when processed and converted into visual display, wouldn't necessarily present the image that the injectee experiences once he's passed beyond the event horizon into Temporal Flux. It's possible that we could pick up his subconscious patterns. In other words, his private fantasy instead of the objective reality.'

Brenton snorted rudely. 'I should have thought,' he said, glancing at the Director, 'that that was the purpose of the exercise. Wherever the injectee happens to find himself, in whatever alternative future, imaginary or otherwise, then that's where he'll be. To speak of "an objective reality" is surely begging the question.'

'That's a valid point,' Karve said, swathed in blue-grey smoke. 'The injectee will create his own alternative future, and, providing we know in advance what it is – and when it is – we can effect retrieval.'

Queghan inclined his head in a small gesture of compliance. 'Point taken. But each of us has an infinite number of subjective realities: we externalize some, repress others. How are we to know which of these – which one specifically – the injectee has chosen to enter? He may not know himself until after injection has taken place. And we can't plot them all, not even cyberthetically.'

Everyone was looking towards Brenton. It was like a game of intellectual ping-pong: a point gained here, a point dropped there. Brenton's thin serious face betrayed nothing of what was going on inside his head. He looked at Queghan for a long moment as if debating how best to reply, then shrugged and waved his hand dismissively. 'Until the technique has been evaluated in the TFC Lab I don't see how we can progress beyond an exchange of personal opinions. I should like to see the Paper before committing myself one way or the other.'

'Very sensible,' Karve said, smiling genially at everyone through the pipe smoke; the subject was now – for the moment – closed.

The sunshine promised by the weather bureau was at last breaking through. Queghan enjoyed it, wandering across the trim lawns to the small artificial lake with its carefully nurtured greenery growing in artful profusion by the water's edge. The sky's glassy reflection lay broken and fragmented on the surface of the water, a shifting pattern of blue sky and cumulus cloud tinged with pink. Such a day as this – with the green grass rippling freshly under the sun and the towers of cloud piled high against the blueness – such a day reminded him of the Battle of Britain, September 1940, Pre-Colonization. He had made a special study of the period, investigated all the Archive material, and run and re-run the old newstapes, and had gained what in the jargon of Myth Technology was known as 'sympathetic identification' with those few crucial months at the beginning of World War II.

Now he conjured up those fresh young faces in their leather helmets and goggles, small groups of three and four lolling on the grass in their fur-lined flying jackets and zippered boots, waiting for the tannoy to hiccup into life and blurt out the order to 'Scramble!'. There was the pungent whiff of glycol on the breeze, the stutter of an engine being tuned by the mechanics, and somewhere faintly in the background from a battered wooden radio with a speaker the shape of a sea-shell – from inside a hut with sunshine slanting through the open doorway – the sound of Vera Lynn singing something about white cliffs and bluebirds.

To Queghan the period had the charm and engaging innocence that was the stuff of myth. He could feel and taste its 'realness' even though it was so long ago that the only reference to it was a supplementary notation in the post-graduation college program. One of the things which intrigued and fascinated him was being able to see with his own eyes how the people looked and behaved; the early Twentieth was notable for being the first period in history to preserve visual documentary evidence of its people, events, customs and social mores. To actually see the pioneers of relativity physics, for instance, how they looked and talked, was an experience which thrilled him.

And for the Myth Technologist it gained in fascination by being a time when such concepts as the Unified Psychic Field Theory hadn't even been dreamt of, much less formulated as a valid scientific premise. Of course they knew, these early pioneers, that energy and matter were interchangeable, but it was as if they possessed knowledge and didn't know what to do with it: they had found the key but didn't know which door it opened, had found the answers but weren't sure of the questions.

The proposal of a Unified Psychic Field – a theoretical framework which would encompass all known psi phenomena and relate them to the laws of the physical universe – didn't arrive until much later; and still the Theory hadn't achieved complete respectability and acceptance. This was one of the aims of Myth Technology and the related area of Meta-Psychical Research. Past and future myths were repositories of collective knowledge and experience, meaningful pieces in the grand jigsaw, and their investigation would reveal the links (or 'leys' as the jargon had it) which connected everything – whether real or abstract, animate or inanimate – with every other thing in the Metagalaxy. There was a secret pattern, an invisible warp and weft of spacetime which could be detected only by psychic means; a gateway existed through which it was possible to pass in order to observe the hidden symmetry, the celestial clockwork ticking quietly away with the flawless precision of a Caesium clock. The gateway was via controlled injection into Temporal Flux, beyond which nothing was positively known – except that it might lead to an infinite series of alternative futures, a multiplicity of universes, each one existing in its own unique spacetime continuum.

Queghan became aware that his wife was trying to contact him. She was several miles distant, at home, alone, and six months pregnant. He pressed the tab in his lapel to acknowledge the signal that Oria's voice murmured in his ear. She had been to see the doctor and he had recommended a course of treatment to correct an endocrine imbalance; there was no cause for alarm, she was feeling perfectly all right, he was not to worry. But Queghan, despite her assurance, couldn't help adopting the role of anxious father-to-be.

'I'll come home now. You and the baby are more important than the Project.'

'It isn't necessary, Chris. Really.' She sounded composed and cheerful. 'He said everything would be fine, providing I take it easy and don't worry. There's really no need for you to leave the Institute.'

'Okay. As long as you do as he says.'

'I promise.'

She was, Queghan felt, telling him the truth, though at this distance it was difficult to know for sure. In any event he didn't want to alarm her by acting hastily and changing the routine; but he would speak to the doctor privately and satisfy himself that all was well. After all, it was their first child: a girl, by mutual agreement.

Brenton looked ill. His dark eyes burned fiercely in an unhealthy complexion which he seemed to have taken pains to acquire; it was as if he had to display his seriousness and dedication like a badge of office. Queghan hadn't realized before how pale and edgy he had become.

They were in the corner of the TFC Lab, Brenton perched uncomfortably on the sill and leaning forward as if to study an invisible object on the floor. Normally he kept very much to himself, preferring his calculus graphs and Minkowskian geometric projections to human company. Brenton was an expert in cyberthetics, a brilliant mind trained in the application of machine intelligence to control and communication systems. He was responsible for the cyberthetic complex which would endow the Injection Vehicle with consciousness so that the Vehicle would possess a live deductive intelligence with the capability to think, to reason, to make decisions. Queghan was the antithesis of Brenton, not at all bright in mathematics: his mind worked intuitively, some might even say (Karla Ritblat for one) erratically.

Brenton said anxiously, 'I think you'll understand this, I hope you will.' He kept looking at the floor. 'It's imperative that I'm selected. I know the machine, we work well together, she would regard anyone else as an intruder. The Director must understand that.'

'She can be programmed to be compatible with anyone's EEG, you yourself made the point in the systems profile,' Queghan said. He tried to register the neurochemical reactions in Brenton's cerebral cortex but there was nothing out of the ordinary taking place. He did detect an unsteady pulse-rate and discharge of adrenalin but these were in keeping with Brenton's agitated condition.

'It's a question of empathy,' Brenton insisted, rocking back and forth, 'a sympathetic understanding. Virtually anyone can be matched with her, the mechanics are fairly simple, but she isn't insensitive to body chemistry and metabolism. It's possible that an adverse reaction could be set up giving rise to malfunction.'

It occurred to Queghan that Brenton's attitude towards the system was almost that of a husband's solicitude for his wife. He wondered whether it would be possible to have a sexual relationship with a cyberthetic machine; there would be nothing physical, of course, but each would be able to achieve sensory stimulation. And a machine having an orgasm was an interesting idea – if one of somewhat dubious morality.

'I think we can rely on the Director to make the right decision,' Queghan said. He had nothing to offer the younger man in the way of consoling phrases; it perplexed him that Brenton should have sought him out and been so confiding. 'You're not married, are you?'

Brenton shook his head.

'Then you have an advantage. You're almost certain to be short-listed, and no doubt Johann will take all the factors into account.'

'There was something else,' Brenton said warily. He slid

down from the sill, looking at Queghan properly for the first time. His face was too unmarked to be so serious; it was as though he'd bought the expression second-hand and it wasn't a particularly good fit.

'Yes?' Queghan said, waiting.

'Do you think you could interpret a coincidence for me? I wouldn't normally impose in this way but I think – well, it might be important. It's something quite ridiculous,' he added in an apologetic tone.

'They often are. Was there a casual relationship that you could see?'

'I don't think so. It's to do with dates. A couple of weeks ago I made a note in my diary – some engagement or other – and a few days later I was told it had been put back. When I checked my diary I found that I'd actually entered the engagement on the correct date, the revised one. I couldn't possibly have known at the time I made the original entry, yet there it was in black and white.'

Queghan was timing his own heartbeat. There was no perceptible change in rhythm or rate. He said, 'Was the second date, the correct one as it turned out, significant in any way? I mean, in some way not directly connected with the engagement?'

Brenton seemed to hesitate for a moment. Then he said, as if reluctantly, 'It's the date of selection.'

'For Project Tempus?'

'Yes.'

'We must consider the rational explanation first,' Queghan said. 'And the rational explanation is that the selection date was on your mind and you inadvertently entered the engagement on the same date. Doesn't that fit the facts?'

'It would do,' Brenton admitted grudgingly, 'except for one thing.'

'And that is?'

'Nobody knew the selection date at the time. The Director didn't make the announcement until a week later.'

'There would seem to be a strong precognitive element there,' Queghan said abstractedly; inwardly he was perfectly calm. There were none of the usual tell-tale symptoms. He went on, 'In any case, if it is meaningful, it would appear to be in your favour.'

'Is there no way you can tell for certain? Isn't there a test of some kind, a procedure . . .'

'I'm afraid not. The whole basis of detecting psi phenomena is that their availability for testing is in inverse ratio to the sophistication of the techniques employed to test them: the nearer we get in scientifically establishing their existence the further away they recede. It's like testing someone's sexual prowess. The fact of telling someone that you're going to evaluate his sexual performance under laboratory conditions is the one thing guaranteed to defeat the purpose of the exercise.'

'But that's the dilemma I'm facing!' Brenton said hopelessly. 'You have the faculty to understand, to appreciate it, whereas I find the whole proposition untenable. Where's the *proof*, I keep asking myself. I need to see the equations, to analyse and interpret them.'

'Well there we are,' Queghan said, and he shrugged. 'If that were feasible, if the equations could be formulated, you and I would become mere abstractions, a neat mathematical formula and not much else. We would cease to exist in any real sense. We'd have as much substance, say, as two fictional characters existing as mind-waves in someone's brain. I can't prove that I exist and neither can you; but we think that we do and that's what matters.'

'I think therefore I am,' Brenton said. 'That's a very shaky scientific proposition,' and Queghan could only agree.

He travelled home in the litter – litter being the LST, or Light Steam Transport. It was noiseless, gave off no fumes, and had a closed energy system that recycled its own waste material. He kept to the controlled M-grid because it was easier to let the litter follow the beam and not have to worry about other vehicles that might get in the way. It was safer, too, just in case he went suddenly into projection. This sometimes happened when he was least expecting it and he didn't relish the thought of being the victim of a litter smash.

56

It had always seemed, ever since he was a child, that the ability to project himself into heightened states of consciousness was very much a mixed blessing. It was a gift not readily understood outside the Institute, and even there it was regarded by some with envy, suspicion, even hostility. It was still, even now, 'unscientific', which was odd when it was considered that psi awareness was really quite common and not confined to a special category of 'gifted' people. It was highly developed in children, for example, but gradually atrophied as they grew older through non-use, in much the same way that a muscle becomes flaccid if not exercised regularly. This general misunderstanding led to resentment, for many people believed that a richness and variety of extrasensory perception was being denied them.

The reality was more prosaic. In most instances, the evidence presented to Queghan's senses was only a piece, a fragment, of a larger, deeper, unfathomable mystery. They thought him capable of miraculous insights which was a simplistic view of what actually happened; true, he was open to the symbols all around, but it was the interpretation of those symbols which was difficult, for they rarely, if ever, formed themselves into a coherent pattern.

As he had tried to explain to Brenton, such manifestations as meaningful coincidence, precognition and the laws of causality (in fact, the entire bag of tricks known as parapsychological phenomena) by their very nature defied assembly into a logical and scientifically-based rationale. This in fact was the aim of the Unified Psychic Field Theory – to establish a structure as the foundation for experimental research. The problem lay in explaining to scientists like Brenton the inherent limitations of any system which tried to impose 'rules' on something so evanescent and intangible as the projection of mind-waves from the one hundred thousand million cells in the human brain.

That this figure approximated to the number of galaxies in the observable universe was one more example of meaningful coincidence. Could it be that the galaxies represented individual cells in one gigantic hyper-brain? Did all energy and matter and its interrelation constitute a single consciousness? If so, then that consciousness was – could only be – God's. And inside his own head the 100,000,000,000 cells might represent another universe, complete with galaxies, nebulae, solar systems and intelligent life-forms.

In Myth Technology this was known as the concept of the Conscious Universe, though no one had managed to devise a theoretical model which could encompass something of such vast proportions and possibilities.

He came off the metalled M-grid and the road became a sandy track which wound between artificial groves fed by an underground piped water supply. The houses were surrounded by electrified fences, and some residents kept dogs, though attacks hadn't been reported for some time. Everyone was mindful of the Manson syndrome, a psychotic illness which seemed to afflict all industrialized societies.

The litter stopped and Queghan opened the canopy. It was like climbing out of a Hurricane. He stepped on to the vinyl driveway, stretching himself under the pleasant warmth of the sun; it seemed the weather bureau had got it right at last. From the audio grill Oria's voice said, 'Black Fox to Red Leader. Rendezvous nineteen hundred hours due west at angles one-seven.'

Queghan smiled and went across the lawn to where his wife lay on the striped lounger; she was naked, on her side, and he could see the dark-brown mole on her left buttock. He kissed her shoulder and moved his hand from her hip to the taut distended belly. 'Has she been troublesome?'

Oria turned to lie on her back. Her breasts had grown over the last month or so. 'No cause for alarm,' she said lightly, smiling up at him. And then, 'Didn't he say so?'

'Who?' Queghan said guiltily.

'The man in the moon.'

'You knew I'd call him.'

'And you knew I'd know.'

'I had to make sure.'

'Yes,' she said pleasantly, closing her eyes.

After a moment, 'The treatment seems simple enough,' Queghan remarked, sitting on the grass at her feet. He plucked a blade of grass and began to chew it. 'When you've had the baby we'll go away.' His grey eyes watched her. 'The three of us.'

'That will be nice,' Oria said. She said this as though he had told her a lie to which she was was politely responding. She could have said anything and it would have meant the same. He had the same feeling as when they'd had an argument, and the areas of blame, forgiveness and remorse hadn't been clearly delineated. There was a distance separating them that was needless and futile; he loved this woman deeply, more than anything on this earth.

'You've never been abroad.' He removed the blade of grass and tickled her foot. 'I could arrange a leave of absence and—'

'Don't you think I ought to have the baby first?'

'That wouldn't be a bad idea.'

'Then why are we talking about it?' she said with ominous quietness. 'We can discuss trips abroad in good time; I don't see the hurry.'

'All right, all right.'

Oria closed her eyes. Her long blonde hair was tied back so that the side of her head gleamed like silver in the sunlight. Before their marriage she had worked at MyTT as a collator in the Archives under Professor Castel; he had few close friends, even among his colleagues, yet Oria had come to like him, and now and then he was invited to dinner. Queghan thought him a cold fish, humourless and rather wearing, but had to admit that in his job he was outstandingly efficient, keeping an eagle eye on the one-and-a-half-million newstapes, audiovisual reels and reference works in the Institute Archives.

Now, watching her, Queghan knew she would resent any attempt on his part at bland consolation: it wasn't only the baby she was worried about.

Oria opened her eyes and looked at him along the length of her body. She said, 'If it was just the baby . . .'

'I know,' Queghan said. 'I know.'

'There's also the fucking Project.'

'The Project isn't that important that we have—'

Oria interrupted him. 'If you're chosen you'll have no alternative but to accept.'

'I can refuse.'

'But you won't.'

'I can always say no,' Queghan insisted patiently.

'We both know that you won't, Chris.' She sat up, her body large and tanned in the direct sunlight. 'We both understand very well that if you're selected you will have to go. There's no alternative.'

Queghan pressed his forehead to the soles of her feet. They were smooth and cool. Her anxiety was because she knew that the odds of the injectee returning were no better than fifty-fifty. This was not an arbitrary computation. It had been calculated with exactitude and certainty. There were conflicting ideas as to why this precise heads-or-tails situation should be: some explained it as a consequence of the Geometrodynamic Law while others thought it more likely to be due to the Theory of Synchronicity*. Queghan felt on a purely intuitive basis that it derived in natural progression from the Lorentz Transformations; in any event the actual cause was irrelevant – it was an inescapable and irreducible mathematical fact, bound up in some way with the physical laws of the Metagalaxy.

The most mysterious aspect was that the odds would never change, neither increase or decrease, no matter how many missions were undertaken. Each mission would be decided on the knife-edge uncertainty of the spin of a coin, irrespective of whether it was the first attempt or the fiftieth or the trillionth. Thus it was pointless to wait until the technology of Temporal Flux injection had exceeded a certain level of sophistication, for this would have zero qualitative effect on the success or failure of any one mission. The phrase 'no time like the present' took on a new aptness, as Johann Karve had been the first to point out.

The sun had fallen below the ragged outline of the trees, throwing long spiky shadows across the lawn. Some of them crept surreptitiously on to the striped lounger, and Queghan felt

* As originally proposed by Jung and Pauli and revised by Conrad and Maxon (Redraft 3rd Edition Sdp).

a shiver of premonition. He got to his feet and stooped to lift Oria into his arms, cradling the swell of her belly against his own. As he did this he was aware that he might never see the child she carried. He had seen it in silhouette, encased in its fluid mucous envelope, and listened to its heartbeat, but perhaps that was all he would ever see or hear or know.

Oria spoke softly, as if there was an eavesdropper nearby – the trees or the creeping shadows. 'There is no alternative, Chris. It isn't technical expertise or knowledge Karve is looking for. The Vehicle is self-programmed, she doesn't require an engineer or a scientist.'

'Brenton wants to go very badly. He's married to the machine. The thought of someone else using her is like seeing his wife being raped.'

'Brenton won't be selected,' Oria said. Her head lay against his shoulder as he carried her up to the house.

'Perhaps not.' Queghan stepped through the sliding door.

'And when you return we will go away, the three of us.'

'Yes,' Queghan said. He stood in the middle of the room, holding his wife and child, knowing (all three of them knowing) that in the existing future he would not return.

Johann Karve had made his reputation at the age of thirty-six when his popular science book *The Hidden Universe* had been published. The ideas he set forth had been current for many years in scientific circles, but it was the first time anyone had brought them together and made any attempt to interrelate them and then to interpolate a whole series of probable consequences. From this he went on to lay the foundation for the field of study which was to become known as Myth Technology, and later he was responsible for the setting up of the Myth Technology Research Institute.

Although superseded by later research, much of the material in *The Hidden Universe* was still relevant, and occasionally Queghan glanced through his well-worn copy in the spirit of someone seeking to retrace the original steps of a scientific discipline for the sheer pleasure it gave him. The early chapters dealt with the origin of Temporal Flux Centres, those areas in space which resulted from the collapse of a neutron star in which the electrons and protons of molecular structure had been crushed by immense gravitational forces to form neutrons – and then crushed yet again to a point of infinite mass and density. Once such a body had formed – a singularity of spacetime curvature – nothing, not even light, could ever escape. Anything nearby would be sucked into this cosmic plughole and crushed out of existence.

The boundary surrounding this spacetime singularity was the event horizon: this was the point of no return and, once inside it, communication with the outside universe was no longer possible.

Karve's analogous explanation of the event horizon was still the clearest and most graphic Queghan had ever come across; it was now classically known as the 'ripple analogy'. Karve pictured a smooth, almost stationary stretch of water which gradually accelerated as it moved downstream towards a weir. If you were to throw a pebble into the water upstream – the still water – the ripples would spread out evenly in all directions, as yet unaffected by the current. Now walk downstream, tossing in pebbles as you go, and as you approach the weir and the flow of water increases, the ripples will cease to make any progress upstream and be pulled downstream: at some point you will have passed the *event horizon*. The ripples (ie lightwaves) cannot resist the downward flow (ie gravitational pull), and therefore can no longer travel to or communicate with the world upstream – the outside universe. At the event horizon itself the speed of the ripple is equal to the downward flow of water and will appear, to the observer on the bank, to stand still; in the same way lightwaves at the event horizon of a Temporal Flux Centre will appear *to the outside observer* to stand still. It can be seen that any material object caught in the downward flow, or gravitational pull, will be unable to resist the force acting upon it and will be dragged inexorably towards the singularity of infinite spacetime curvature.

Although the earlier chapters were interesting, it was towards the end of *The Hidden Universe*, the chapters dealing with the wider philosophical implications of Temporal Flux, that Queghan now found most stimulating, and in particular the section devoted to the probability of multiple universes as constituent parts of a greater all-embracing Metagalaxy. Karve had written:

'In our investigation of Temporal Flux situations throughout the observable universe we must be aware that our attention is inward-directed. In other words, we are assuming that our universe is an infinite spatio-temporal structure and not, as we know it to be, one universe of a multiple series existing in the total Metagalaxy, which comprises all matter which is visible, invisible, and anti-matter. Expressed in simple terms, we are like a man on a small desert island, surrounded by many more islands, who busies himself only with what is happening on his own island and is oblivious to those all around. His gaze is inward-directed, and until he simply turns and looks out to sea he will remain in ignorance of the larger world outside which contains many more, similar islands.

'We know, within fairly precise limits, the amount of matter required to form a collapsar and then eventually Temporal Flux. This is 8.41 solar masses, and, even Pre-Colonization, the astro-physicists weren't far wide of the mark in their calculations. Theoretically of course *any* object is capable of achieving Temporal Flux providing the nuclear structure has been broken down and compressed to infinite density, but in practice there is a certain critical mass below which this does not occur. Within the observable universe (our desert island) we see a large number of bodies whose mass is above the critical limit, and these will, in due course, achieve a condition of Temporal Flux. Let us now direct our gaze out to sea. We become aware immediately of the possibility that the observable universe, our island, is one of many. It is not, *sine qua non*, unique.

'If it is not unique, therefore, we must regard it as a finite body in a sea of infinite spacetime, a single island among many. Upon examination of our universe we find a very curious and inexplicable fact. The average density of matter in the universe is 10^{-29} grams per cubic centimetre. The radius of the observable universe is 10^{10} light-years. If, based on these figures, we calculate the critical mass and size required to achieve Temporal Flux for a body of this type we arrive at the surprising answer that the density must be 10^{-29} grams per cubic centimetre and the radius 10^{10} light-years. It is perfectly correct to surmise, then, that the observable universe is of sufficient mass and density, and within the critical (Schwarzschild) radius to achieve Temporal Flux. Though we do not know it and have no way of telling, we may *already* inhabit a region of Temporal Flux which may in itself be part of another universe.

'This hypothesis can be extended indefinitely. The greater universe of which our universe forms a single region of Temporal Flux may itself be a region of Temporal Flux in another, still larger universe. And so on, *ad infinitum.* Conversely, the numerous Temporal Flux Centres in our own universe might contain, or lead to, other universes, each of which has regions of Temporal Flux leading to other universes which have regions of Temporal Flux leading to ... So it is conceivable that the "master plan" is constructed on the lines of an infinite series of Chinese boxes, one inside the other, each universe separate and self-contained and linked, like interconnecting doors, by regions of Temporal Flux.

'Though it might appear so at first glance, this is not at all fanciful or far-fetched. We know from our measurements and computations that the Metagalaxy should contain far more material than can be accounted for by visual and electromagnetic observation. Where is it to be found? In what hidden regions is the missing material contained?

'We can only assume that via Temporal Flux – "down the rabbit hole", so to speak – we shall enter into and discover those hidden regions, this accumulation of missing material. There can be no guarantees, no confident predictions; and whoever goes down the rabbit hole may never come back to tell us how right or wrong we are in our speculations.'

It was not the possibility of a multiplicity of universes which disturbed Queghan: the science of Myth Technology more or less tacitly accepted their existence. Mythographers over the years had combed the records of ancient civilizations and religions, ranging as far afield as the study of occultism, spiritualism, psychiatric case studies, Jungian texts, paranormal phenomena and UFO-ology – all in search of evidence to show that the everyday physical universe open to our senses is only one manifestation of underlying reality. Queghan could accept this; what he had difficulty in believing was Karve's idea of the universe, our universe, as a region of Temporal Flux. It followed logically, he couldn't refute Karve's hypothesis; and yet the implications were, to say the least, unsettling.

The dynamics of myth and legend owed as much to intuitive insight as to analytical reasoning. It was no good accepting the validity of an argument intellectually if it wasn't felt to be true emotionally, through the senses. Queghan's talent – perhaps his only real contribution – lay in his instinctive recognition of a basically sound concept. Just as he possessed the sensory equipment to detect changes in someone's mood and emotional state by minute shifts in their body chemistry, in the same way he reacted to the underlying truth or falseness of a statement, supposition or theoretical construction. But what if Karve was right? Could the universe sustain itself as a figment of the imagination?

That night he had a dream. In the dream he was an invisible onlooker (he was conscious of this) observing his wife and child in the garden. The child was playing on the grass, rolling a coloured ball, and, when it was rolled back, trying to stop it. But each time the child reached out he lost his balance and fell over, laughing at this and making a great game of it all.

And in a strange way Queghan was both inside and outside the dream. He watched the dream unfolding and he was also aware that the Dream Tape at his bedside had automatically switched itself on and was recording his brain activity. He even had the presence of mind to think, 'I shall play the tape back in the morning and find out what this means.' In the dream, too, he wondered what it meant, watching his wife and – presumably – their child playing on the grass. It was unlike a dream, in that everything was so natural and real, the trees creaking and rustling, the faint whirr of insects, the sunlight bathing the lawn in vibrant green. His wife looked well and happy; had everything worked out all right in the end?

Then he saw the stranger on the striped lounger. The stranger was a man, unknown to him, with a long lean face and white hair, and he didn't seem to be any particular age. He was lying back with his eyes closed, his body perfectly relaxed, his hands resting placidly in his lap. Oria looked up, smiling, and said something to the stranger. Unfortunately the dream wasn't equipped with a soundtrack and while Queghan could see her lips plainly move he couldn't decipher what she was saying. The stranger opened his eyes and answered her. Oria rose to her feet and went over to him: she was barefoot and her legs were brown: in contrast, the stranger was very pale, his eyes dark and deep-set. His inertness reminded Queghan of someone he knew, like having a familiar name on the tip of the tongue, and he wanted to break out of the dream so that he could bring the stranger's identity to mind. But he was too involved in the dream and didn't want to shatter the delicate fleeting surface.

Oria stood in front of the stranger, her toes (Queghan noted) curled in the grass and her feet turned slightly inwards, like those of a schoolgirl, which was her way of standing. She stood before him and opened her hand to reveal a small yellow flower, a buttercup. The stranger smiled and when Oria said something to him lifted his head so that she could hold the flower under his chin. She twirled it and bent forward to look for the golden reflection. At this point the image shivered and broke.

He wanted to drift back into the dream but, as usual, the harder he tried the further it receded. How much of it was precognition he didn't know. Perhaps it was simply the random confusion of the real and the imaginary in the way that dreams weave actual memories with abstract thoughts, the repository of all the unspent neurological impulses frittering about in the brain. But there had to be an interpretation: he would transcribe the tape and isolate the main components of the dream.

In the morning he took the tape from the machine and ran it through the audiovisual Indexer. The display would allow him to plot the alpha and delta phases of sleep; but when he put the tape in the Indexer the screen remained blank. Nothing had been recorded, not the faintest trace. In a fury he wrenched the spools from the Indexer and went to the window, intending to throw them into the garden like Jack's bag of beans. But the curtains got in the way; they tangled and frustrated him, and as he struggled with the enveloping material Oria gripped his shoulders and said, 'Chris, Chris!'

She was holding him and he was lying in bed covered in sweat, his hands emmeshed in the covers. 'It's all right,' Oria said.

Queghan looked at the Dream Tape by his bedside: the counter registered zero: he had forgotten to plug it in."

4

Brainstorm

The airship *Torremolinos* moved gracefully like a fat silver cigar over the red ocean at a height of nine hundred feet, tacking south-west with the help of the trade winds. The bulk of the ship comprised an hexagonal wooden frame over which canvas had been tightly drawn and the whole assembly inflated with hydrogen fluoride, a highly unstable gas which was corrosive, poisonous and liable to ignite at the slightest spark. For this reason inflammatory materials were not allowed on board, and the passengers and crew were issued with rope-soled shoes which would cause no friction on the wooden decks and stairways.

The gondola suspended beneath the canopy on thick ropes had a complement of ten crew and thirty-five passengers, most of whom were paramilitary with a scattering of medikal personnel; for most of the passengers it was their first trip in the air, a wonderful, breathtaking experience which overcame the fear of sailing through the clouds in such a new-fangled contraption and one so unproven that even King Jimmy K (who as a rule was the first to try anything new) had declined an invitation to take a trial flight.

The observation porch on the lowest of the three decks gave splendid views of the terrain: the cities, towns and countryside, and now the ocean, swelling and rippling beneath them, the purple peaks caught by the wind and making a pattern of opaque rainbows, their colours mingled and muddy. The voyage would last three weeks, mostly ocean-going, and at the end of it the continent of Australasia, and Psy-Con. The passengers had settled back to relax and enjoy the trip, falling in gradually with the easy routine and slow-passing days, though

68

Dr Mathew Black hadn't found relaxation easy to come by. It wasn't only his charge or the responsibility that this entailed, it was the disquieting knowledge that the Medikal Direktorate Authority had assigned two guards to accompany them, which meant that not only the deportee but Black too was under day-to-day surveillance. His preliminary report to the MRA concerning the patient – veiled and allusive as it was – had been enough to cause a flutter of alarm, the rapid outcome being that Black was instructed to accompany the patient to Psy-Con and oversee the initial stages of indoctrination. The directive had put an abrupt stop to Black's pioneering work in Gestalt Treatment, which was annoying when the initial results had seemed so promising. Evidently the MDA thought them spurious, dangerous or subversive; new ideas, as Black continually and bitterly reminded himself, were not welcome.

On the third day he sat with Q in the observation porch, watching the slow drift of the ocean through the slanting windows. The constant twittering clamour of canaries filled the air. Further along the saloon the two uniformed guards hovered lugubriously over the proceedings, their arms folded beneath their capes like a couple of large black crows gone to roost. A ship moved on the ocean, at the apex of an arrow pointing eastwards, and when it had disappeared from view Black ventured to remark, 'I hope you realize what a privilege it is to be deported by airship. It's unusual for patients to receive this sort of treatment.' His voice, even to his own ears, had a thin sneering whine to it.

'I'm flattered,' Q replied, 'and suitably impressed.'

Black smiled sardonically. He felt himself incapable of saying or thinking anything that wasn't tainted by cynicism and self-disgust. 'I suppose this is all rather tame stuff compared with your "mythic projections" or whatever you call them.'

'On the contrary.' Q tried to adjust his position in the wicker chair but was hampered by the ropes binding his arms and legs. Whenever he moved too abruptly it tightened the noose around his neck. He gave up the struggle and subsided against the ropes. 'The experience is stimulating, if a mite uncomfortable.'

'I'm sorry about that.' Black leaned across and slackened the noose a fraction. 'Standard procedure.'

'I thought it might be.'

'Don't be smart. I could have you locked away on the upper deck next to the gas chamber. The first sign of a leakage and you wouldn't last thirty seconds.'

Q inclined his head towards the bamboo cages hanging from the bulkhead; they were strung all over the airship. 'That's the reason for the canaries, I suppose. If there's a leak they'll detect it and sound a warning.'

'Yes,' Black said testily. 'But I imagine you would serve the same purpose just as well. You're not immune to hydrogen fluoride, are you?'

'Wouldn't the Authority be rather unhappy if I was dead on arrival? I got the impression they were keen to rehabilitate me in the place you call Psy-Con.'

Black gave a cold, slow smile. 'Do you know what Psy-Con is? Do you know what it stands for? Psychological Concentration Camp. I'm afraid rehabilitation isn't on the program of events. It might have been mentioned, but it's the Authority's method of pacifying deportees prior to shipment. It calms them if they believe they're to receive treatment.'

'Are they ill to begin with?'

'Of course they're ill,' Black snapped. 'Why do you think we need Psy-Con if we didn't have the people to fill it? Australasia's a big place but it already has an inmate population of twenty-eight million. It's a wise move, don't you think, herding them all into one place?'

'Are they dangerous?'

'They're a disruptive influence, they spread alarm among the populace.' He added slyly, 'That's why the Authority want you out of the way. It's people like you, people who babble, people with hallucinations, who cause all the trouble.' When he became agitated his sibilant lisp was pronounced.

'In that case I shall have to be careful what I say.'

'Too late for that,' Black said smugly. 'You probably don't remember, but back in the sanatorium you ranted and raved like a madman. The stuff that came out, you wouldn't credit.' He sat back in the chair, idly surveying the red ocean through the slanting windows. The sun was a vast yellow orb in the hazy azure sky. He said morosely, 'They should have let me continue the experiment. Galvanology has a tremendous future in medikal science. The Authority are so damn pig-headed—'

He checked himself and glanced along the saloon: several people were dozing in wicker chairs but the two black-uniformed guards were for the moment absent. He would have to be careful, remain tight-lipped when others were near by. There was no telling who might be taking note of the conversation.

'You regard everything I said as hallucination, then?' Q asked. He noticed that Black's fingernails were ragged.

'What else? You're cursed with too much imagination, like most of the other deportees. I wanted to purge you of all that stuff, get you to puke it out. You rambled on for hours but there must be a lot more to come out.' He tilted back in his chair. 'In a way it was quite an interesting story. Your mind must be a cess-pool of non-associative thoughts and random ideas. The thing I couldn't understand was that this other realm, or whatever it was, where all this was supposed to be taking place, didn't seem to be here on Earth IVn. It's a syndrome I haven't come across before—'

'What did you say?'

Black sighed. 'I said it was a syndrome I haven't encountered before in my case-studies.'

'You said "here on Earth IVn". Is that where we are, on Earth IVn?'

Black's face creased into a strained and weary smile. 'If you ask questions like that they'll put you straight into the High Intensity Complex. Psy-Con is bad enough without winding up there.'

'Let me ask another foolish question. Why is it called Earth IVn?'

'Why is anything called anything?' Black said irritably. 'Why is the ocean red, the sky azure? This is Earth IVn because it's Earth IVn. What cod-laddle you talk.' He lowered his voice. 'I advise you not to ask such questions. If the Authority get to hear of them they'll slap you in the Complex, and there's not a gingy crole I can do to help you.'

Q then did something which infuriated Black: he smiled.

'And don't grin like that! They'll think you're a loon and feed you to the alligators, and I might just let them.'

'Why should you want to help me, anyway?' Q said. He tried to work his hands to restore the circulation: the skin on his wrists was pinched cruelly by the ropes. 'Aren't you putting yourself at risk?'

'Maybe.' Black looked over his shoulder. He said, 'The Authority don't agree, but I think your ramblings should be investigated further. There's an element of Logik in them which I find interesting; and this "other-world" syndrome is something I haven't heard of before.' He paused and clicked his fingers. ' "Other-world" syndrome. I like that.'

'You're beginning to believe in my mythic projections, after all. They're not simply the ravings of a madman.'

'Do you take me for a fool?' Black's thin dark face was twisted with contempt. 'I'm a medikal doktor, not a quack. If I believed in them I'd be as crazy as you are. I've had patients who believed they were reincarnations of Franko, and others who thought they were second cousin to President Disraeli. Do you expect me to believe every bit of nonsense I hear?'

Q moved himself stiffly in the chair, attempting to stretch his pale thin body. He was a giant compared to Black, almost half as tall again as the slight, narrow-shouldered, lisping man.

Q said: 'There's one question you haven't answered.'

'Well?' Black said sullenly.

'Where am I from?'

Was there, Black wondered, a hint of amused provocation in those flat grey eyes? He decided that there wasn't, but at the same time a great constricting gorge of fury rose up in his chest and threatened to suffocate him; he felt his grip slackening, the world sliding.

'We know you came from the sea,' he managed to say at last. 'It was all in the report. The Captain of the *Slave Trader* was most thorough.'

'He said I came from the sea, but did he say how I got there?'

Those flat grey eyes were fixed on Black and he had to give way, to lower his head and gaze down on the ocean. Sarah had been right, the fellow was a dangerous influence on a calm, self-collected personality. Black felt intimidated and strangely weak: it was as though (had he believed it possible) his energy and purpose were being drained away. By God, if only they had let him continue the Gestalt Treatment he would have made the fellow suffer!

'Did the question never occur to you?' Q inquired mildly.

'Of course it did.'

'But you never sought an answer.'

The canaries in their cages were twittering, filling the airship with their noise. The yellow sun blazed in through the windows, its rays illuminating the dust-motes circulating in the still air.

Black said, 'Where you came from is of no consequence. The MDA concerns itself with practicalities, not with vague curiosity or blind guesswork. We don't need to know where you came from, it isn't important. We live in the real world, not in some—'

'What about the things you don't understand?'

Black said, 'Sarah was right when she said you were disruptive. I'm beginning to think the Complex is the best place for you.'

'Yet you have an idea that my "babblings" might be closer to the truth than the Authority are prepared to admit. You abide by their rules, but underneath you're not sure—'

'Non-associative claptrap,' Black said, waving his hand dismissively. 'My only interest is in the pursuit of medikal knowledge. You just happened to be available. If it hadn't been you, some other patient would have done just as well.'

Q tried to ease his cramped position but the ropes held him firmly. 'Does Dr Hallam agree with this philosophy? Does she think that everyone who has non-associative thoughts is fit only for Psy-Con?'

'Dr Hallam did believe that.' Black gazed down on to the ocean. He said, 'Sarah's dead. The rats got her.'

*

The *Torremolinos* sailed on sedately through azure skies, the quiet days unbroken by anything more remarkable than the occasional vessel below, its sails full and yellow under the glare of the sun; once, they saw a pirate ship, the skull-and-cross-bones plainly discernible to the naked eye, but they were too far from land to telegraph its position, and even had they been able to do so, the King's fleet would have taken days to intercept.

It was approaching high summer in the southern hemisphere, the days becoming longer and the air noticeably warmer: the trades stiffened at these latitudes so that the airship picked up speed as it neared the Australasian continent. There was a daily contest to see who could estimate the distance travelled, though the Captain, had he been prepared to admit it, wasn't altogether certain of the precise mileage. But it was a harmless diversion and the Captain saw to it that everyone won the contest at least once on the voyage.

Each evening, after dinner, the passengers retired to the saloon deck and played bridge or read outdated periodicals or simply gazed out upon the ocean, its colour fading with the darkness until it became a black shifting mass – on the western horizon a faint line marking the division between sea and sky, dusk and nightfall.

Dr Black wrote up his notes, taking care not to be too explicit lest the Authority suspect him of having a more than professional interest in the patient; he was there to observe, to keep the patient under control, to ensure that the initial phase of screening was carried out smoothly and according to regulations. He certainly wasn't there to further his career by investigating such new-fangled techniques as galvanology and the like.

He wrote: 'The tendencies exhibited by the patient conform to the general pattern (imaginative leaps, etc) but diverge in two respects which are perhaps worth noting. First, the patient displays few, if any, signs of agitation. His behaviour is subdued, almost dreamlike, and he accepts without question or complaint the situation in which he finds himself. Secondly, his hallucinatory flights are characterized by an unusually high degree of coherence: that is to say, his imaginings, however fanciful, are consistent *within themselves* and do contain a weird Logik which . . .'

He was about to write 'gains in conviction with the accumulation of data' but hesitated, his pen hovering over the page. He couldn't write that, they would smell a rat for sure. (Poor Sarah.) Instead, he would put something about 'standard procedure', which was sure to please them. How careful one had to be! His hands felt suddenly cold, there was a dryness in the roof of his mouth; it had occurred to him out of the blue that there might be an ulterior motive in having assigned him to accompany Q to Psy-Con. And why two guards? He felt the sweat prickle on his forehead. Why not one, or three? Was he being stupid to get so worked up into a panic; and then he decided that, stupid or not, he couldn't think of a single logikal reason why, on reaching Psy-Con, he shouldn't be imprisoned there too. The Authority worked that way, they led people blithely along and then, quick as a wink, everything changed, the benign smiling faces became scowls and you found yourself in the High Intensity Complex.

Somebody put a hand on his shoulder and said, 'Dr Black.' He jumped.

'Yes?' Black said, ashen-faced.

The guard said, 'I think you'd better come along. The patient seems to be having a fit.'

Black followed him up to the middle deck where the sleeping-cubicles were arranged along each side of the gondola; there was just enough room for a bed and a wicker chair; a small bureau folded down from the wall containing two drawers and a swivel mirror, and underneath the bed a large flat skip was provided for the passenger's clothing.

Q was strapped to the bed and the bed was bolted down, but it seemed to Black that, even so, the patient might wrench the entire assembly from the deck. He was paler than before, his flesh transparent, with the bones, musculature and blood vessels clearly visible, his eyeballs turned upwards into his head so that the sockets were a blind staring white. There was a foam on his lips, flecks of it flying off with his exhalations.

75

'You better do something,' one of the guards said unemotionally. 'He's going to tear that bed loose.'

Black said, 'It's an excess of poison in the blood. We'll have to bleed him.'

'Well, for God's sake, do it,' the other guard said. 'He's your responsibility.'

'Hold him down,' Black said. He went to fetch his bag from the next cubicle. The guards were kneeling on Q's arms, but they couldn't control his body which, even though bound by the straps, was jerking frenziedly from side to side, bucking like a stranded fish.

'Hold him, hold him,' Black said. 'I'll try for the forearm.' He took the pointed instrument and was about to make an incision when, all at once, there was no need to do anything. The patient went rigid, his breathing stopped and he lay still. The guards released his arms which fell either side of the bed, slack as a doll's.

'Is he dead?' one of the guards asked.

'If he is, he'll make the angels happy,' said the other. 'He's got a hard on like a flagpole.'

Black fumbled for the pulse and found it, weak and erratic, and when he checked the heart it was fluttering like a frightened dove's. He said: 'This is very similar to a state of galvanic shock.' He turned to one of the guards. 'Has he been given stimulants of any kind?'

'I gave him nothing,' the man said stolidly.

'What happened exactly?' Black demanded. (He was in charge now, the doktor with his mysterious rituals, and he felt a new surge of confidence and authority.)

'I was doing the hourly check, according to regulations, and when I opened the door he was trying to sit up, and staring at me and babbling like a madman. I tried to restrain him but he went berserk, gabbling something about "time" as near as I could make out. Then I came and got you.' He scratched his chin with a broad thumbnail. 'Is he a loonie?'

'I can't discuss the patient's case-history,' Black said officiously. 'He said something about "time". What was it? Try and remember.'

76

The guard frowned. He stared at the wall for a moment. His face cleared. 'He said "There shall be time no longer". Whatever that's supposed to mean.'

'That was all? Nothing else?'

'There was, but I couldn't catch it. I told you, he was babbling, it sounded like nonsense to me.'

'Yes,' said Black. 'It would to you.' He leaned over the patient and raised one of his eyelids. 'There's nothing we can do except let him rest.' He adjusted the straps, tightening them another notch. 'Keep checking every hour but don't disturb him.'

'*Disturb* him!' one of the guards said. 'He disturbs *me*.'

Black stepped into the corridor. 'This is a medikal matter and so I don't expect you to understand.' He stretched himself to his full five feet four. 'If you need me I shall be in the lower saloon,' and went quickly away while he still had the advantage.

Q appeared to have fully recovered the next morning and didn't seem to be suffering any ill effects following his 'attack'. He was fed, as usual, by one of the guards who performed the task with ill grace, shovelling the mush into the patient's mouth and hardly caring how much went in and how much ran down his chin and dropped into his lap. But Q never complained; he seemed indifferent to physical discomfort, unfailingly calm and composed.

Dr Black had pondered the meaning of the phrase which Q had uttered during his seizure, but if it meant anything at all it was lost on him. He felt better this morning, his depression had lifted and he no longer – for the time being – feared the guards or was too perturbed about the arrival of the *Torremolinos* in Australasia.

After breakfast he sat beneath the subdued canaries on the saloon deck and leafed through the Medikal Direktory he always carried with him. It listed four main causes of seizure: apoplexy, dementia, epilepsy and poisoning of the bloodstream. Any of these might have been the cause, there was no way of knowing, and even with the necessary instruments it was largely a matter of personal interpretation. What one doktor might have diagnosed as dementia another could just as easily and with as much reason have classified as epilepsy. Providing the explanation sounded logikal and didn't conflict with the prevailing Authority directive it would be accepted without question.

The phrase still bothered him – 'There shall be time no longer'. There shall be time no longer for what? he asked himself. Was time running out and, if so, who for? For the patient? Black could only suppose that at last Q was beginning to realize what lay in store for him, had woken up to the cold unpalatable fact that Psy-Con was a place from which no one ever returned.

Black looked around him. He regretted that there were no females on board: he was dying for a quick thrust and a poke. Since Sarah had ceased to be available he had cojoined on several occasions with Miss Jardine, the large-busted blonde receptionist (once underneath his desk among the rat droppings while the Registrar hammered impotently on the door); and he was feeling the pain of withdrawal quite acutely. But until landfall there was nothing to be done. In lieu of anything better he would have to settle for his nightly handslide and like it.

A glass tipped over and rolled off the table. The airship had tilted – or the gondola itself had swung askew under a sudden gust of wind. The bamboo cages rocked in unison and set the canaries off to a burst of shrill twittering. The First Officer appeared, treading cautiously between the tables, and assured everyone that there was no cause for alarm. In these latitudes, he explained, the thermal currents were unpredictable and sometimes upset the trim. Everything was under control.

As he said this, there was a violent shudder followed by a wild swaying motion which upset more glasses and sent them tumbling to the deck. 'We're re-aligning the trim,' said the First Officer with a brave smile. 'Please don't be alarmed.'

'Progress has its price,' Black observed, and the First Officer gave him a dark look.

Then the airship seemed to right itself and sailed on as calmly as before. It had been a meteorological aberration, nothing more. They were due to sight the northern coastline of Australasia later in the day, and following that there would be two days of overland flight before berthing at the reception centre, situated in the Eastern Province.

At noon they passed over the mangrove swamps at a height of fifteen hundred feet. What lay ahead was barren desert baking in the heat of a relatively cool 107 degrees, inhabited only by scorpions, centipedes, two-headed King snakes and, further inland, the high-security settlements surrounded by wire enclosures and the alligator pits. The alligators were sunning themselves in the ooze, their wide flat bodies flaked with dried grey mud. Black had the patient brought to the observation porch, and together they gazed out on the mile after mile of single-storey wooden huts laid in symmetrical blocks of eight stretching away as far as the eye could see.

'This is the High Intensity Complex,' Black explained. 'Once you arrive here you never get out. Everyone sent here is a terminal case.'

'They're dangerous people, are they?' Q inquired, as if out of polite interest.

'Very dangerous.'

'Violent?'

Black looked surprised. 'Of course they're not violent. In any case, violence isn't a crime. It's their thoughts which are dangerous: non-associative, subversive, against the King, the State, the Authority. If these people were allowed to roam freely, to think and do as they wished, they would be a disruptive influence on society. We can't allow that. We're entering an age of great scientific progress, the Mekanikal Era some call it, and these people want to wreck and destroy it.'

'In what way?' Q was curious.

'In any way they can,' Black said vehemently. 'The facts are well documented. That's why the Royal Charter was issued which directs the MDA to find some effective means of control and stamp down hard on the reversionaries before they get out of hand.'

'Am I such a threat?' Q asked in mild surprise.

'You must see that you are.' Black was deeply intense when he had a point to get across. He became feverish and light-headed, his eyes rolled about in his small dark face and he lisped breathlessly. He rushed on, 'Anyone outside the norm cannot be tolerated for obvious reasons. You either adhere to the rule of Logik or you must accept the consequences; there is no middle course. You – by your appearance, your conduct, your thought processes – are a million miles away from the norm and therefore constitute a threat. There is no alternative but Psy-Con.'

Q looked down on the huts, the wire enclosures, the alligator pits. The vast black shadow of the airship moved across like a dark stain soaking into the landscape, blotting out the sun in a brief man-made eclipse. In the distance the heat haze was a shimmering yellow fog, distorting the linear perspective and turning it into a complex fragmented display. The eye was deceived, confused and lost in the shifting patterns and indices of refraction. Anything approximating to life out there must needs have the mind of an ant and the metabolism of a reptile.

Black was jotting something down in his notebook. He looked up, preoccupied, and said, 'Do you recall what happened last night? Can you remember any of it?'

'Yes,' Q said. 'I remember everything.'

'You had some sort of fit and apparently you were trying to say something, only the guards couldn't make head or tail of it. It struck me as being very similar to a state of galvanic shock.'

Q gazed at him unblinkingly. He said, 'There is a similarity between the two. It's caused by the neurons discharging an abnormally high amount of electrical energy into the cerebellum, which produces what you would probably describe as a brainstorm. The effects can vary but usually there's a seizure which results in convulsions, periods of staring, occasional babbling, uncontrollable rage and eventually unconsciousness.'

'You know the symptoms very well,' Black said, leaning forward. 'It isn't the first time this has happened to you.'

The patient smiled. 'No, not the first.'

'Does it happen very often?'

'Now and then. Whenever I feel it's necessary.'

'You can control it?' Black said, his dark eyebrows knitting together. 'You can induce it yourself?'

'Sometimes, yes. And other times it happens without my being aware of it; there is a measure of control.'

'But how?' Black was engrossed. 'What do you have to do?'

'The methods are rather complex but the simplest way is by using a substance called Dilantin.'

'I've never heard of it.'

'I should be surprised if you had,' Q said, smiling again.

'Oh, I see. Another of your mythic projections or whatever you call them. You spirit this make-believe substance out of thin air and swallow it down and it produces an imaginary effect.' He too was smiling, but tightly and without humour.

'The effect isn't at all imaginary, as you've seen for yourself.'

'Maybe,' Black said sceptically. 'But I still don't see the point of it all. Supposing you can induce this condition, so what? I've seen patients have seizures before now, there's nothing too remarkable about that.'

'To the observer that's perfectly true. But during the Peak Experience – or seizure, as you would call it – theta waves are produced. What you might describe as "mind stuff".'

'Go on,' said Black, the suspicion of a grin lurking at the corners of his mouth. 'Tell me about "mind stuff".'

' "Mind stuff" is the fabric of spacetime—' Q said. He seemed to hold his breath for a moment, almost as if he had experienced a sudden pain.

'What's the matter, cat got your tongue?' Black asked with a sneering grin.

Q didn't hear him. He said absently, 'I didn't know any of this yesterday, nothing about neurons or Dilantin . . . I didn't know any of it.' He seemed lost, bemused.

'You'll remember next how you came to be adrift in the ocean, no doubt,' said Black, snapping his notebook shut. 'Any more imaginary leaps you'd like to get off your chest? Any more non-associative cod-laddle? There's no doubt about it, you're heading straight for the High Intensity Complex. Once they've rammed you through the screening process you'll be classified as a subversive risk, Grade A. Nothing I can do about it, not a thing. You've heard my advice to keep your mouth

81

shut, and yet you babble on like a loonie. Don't say I didn't warn you. I did my best. Don't say – Bladdering shtank!'

The patient was out of control. His limbs were jerking like rods and he was in danger of strangling himself with the noose. Black leaped forward and slackened it just as Q began to speak, the words coming out fast and low between the flecks of foam. The doktor, having no choice, listened.

5

Stasis

"The Scenario Planning Symposium was attended by over four hundred delegates from the fourteen planetary and planetoidal states, all of them in the related sciences of Myth Technology and MetaPsychical Research. The two sciences ran parallel in the pursuit of the same ultimate goal but were dissimilar in method and approach; on the one hand MetaPsychical Research ('MetaPsychics' as the newsmedia called it, to the intense dislike of those involved) was concerned with establishing a MetaPsychical Code which would define the neurological connection between man's sensory perceptions and the physical nature of the universe. It was hoped that this would evolve into a pre-dictive as opposed to a post-dictive science, because without this capability the Myth Technologists would find themselves in the position of someone floundering around helplessly in a magnetic snowstorm.

Myth Technology was more into the field of practical investigation of the infinite series of mythical futures which were known to exist and not to exist at one and the same time – a paradox which could only be explained in terms of relativistic physics. Part of this work was the attempt to construct a Unified Psychic Field Theory which would relate all known psychic forces with the four prime energy sources of the Metagalaxy. In this there was an overlap with the MetaPsychical Code, which some Myth Technologists regarded as part of the Unified Psychic Field Theory; but where the two fields of study did come together was in the shared responsibility and enthusiasm for Project Tempus. It was a joint commitment which required the pooling of every resource, technical and financial, of the governmental agencies responsible for cosmological exploration. The purpose of the Symposium was to assess the work done so far and to recommend the optimum critical path for further research; in practical terms it was the final meeting before Project Tempus moved from the realm of abstract speculation into the real world of hard uncompromising fact.

As Director of MyTT Johann Karve was there as the coordinating chairman and floor leader; Martin Brenton, architect of the cyberthetic Injection Vehicle, was also present, and so too was Karla Ritblat, who as head of the Psycho-Med Faculty had the final say in the selection of the injectee. Professor Milton Blake, the leading theorist in MetaPsychical Research, was there to present the latest conclusions in the contentious area of predictive technology; and one of the main talking points was his Paper *Concerning the Hypothesis of Determining Problematical Futures.* Everything depended, the Paper emphasized, on the injectee having the facility to project his thoughts on a consistent world-line through the spatio-temporal barrier; only then would it be possible to locate, identify and plot the injectee's world-point – in other words, home in and effect retrieval when necessary.

Another problem discussed in the Paper was that of time dilation,* which was the effect experienced by anything of mass approaching the ergosphere of a Temporal Flux Centre. This meant that the injectee's time-scale would slow down almost to a stop; his ageing process would be practically negligible, while for those observing him (direct observation was in fact impossible) time would pass in the usual way. The problem – all too real as Blake had pointed out – was that the injectee, if and when he returned, would find himself several hundred, possibly several thousand years in the future. Everything and everyone he had known – his home, his family, his friends – would have been lost, gone forever in the mists of time; if he had a continuing line of descendants he would be able to shake the hand of his grandchild fifty, perhaps a hundred, generations removed from his own time. He would be condemned to the future, never able to return, except in the mythical sense.

* For the mathematics relating to time dilation, interested readers should refer to Appendix I.

Milton Blake was a lithe man with a handsome Negroid face and slim expressive hands. He smiled a good deal, and it was difficult to think of anyone he could not charm if he put his mind to it. Even Karla Ritblat couldn't help the occasional sidelong glance and tentative smile, a flush of colour in her hollow cheeks. Blake asked Queghan about his wife and the child they were expecting; how many children did they plan to have?

'Maybe one will be enough to bust the stress rating.' Queghan said, which evoked laughter from the dozen or so people present. It was an informal group relaxing in one of the recreation rooms after a morning session.

'Seven is a lucky number,' Blake said, winking at Karve. 'Especially for a mythographer.'

'If I could predict that well, there'd be need for a Symposium. I'd plot my own world-line and stick to it like a shuttle timetable.'

'At least he made the shuttles run on time,' said one wag.

Karve said, 'If you were really that good, Chris, you could inject yourself and stay behind to tell us where the hell you'd got to.'

'You mean go and not go?'

'Why not?' Karve said. 'Transmit a few billion tachyons into Temporal Flux and just sit back twiddling your thumbs and waiting for yourself to report.'

'Slight problem,' said Milton Blake. 'He'd find himself reporting back before he'd sent the message, so he'd have the answer before asking the question.'

This was a reference to the time-reversing particle known as the tachyon, which, along with the mu-geon, constituted the only sub-microscopic particles yet discovered which broke the ground rules of Einsteinian physics: both were without mass or electric charge and could therefore defy the basic principle that nothing could travel with a velocity exceeding lightspeed — 300,000 kilometres per second. The tachyon, travelling faster than lightspeed, arrived before it departed (which was the same thing as time reversal), the classic case, as Karve put it, of a particle picking itself up by its own bootstraps. The mu-geon was the gravitational particle which made up the fabric of spacetime curvature: it was the basis for the science of Geometrodynamics, which dealt with the concepts of curved space and curved time – the geometric construction arising out of the force exerted by any massive body, such as a star, on the empty space surrounding it.

As for the tachyon, paranormal sensory perception could not exist without it. It was believed that the mind-waves of certain people were capable of detecting tachyons and utilizing the information they contained; thus it was possible to have advance warning of an event before it took place. This led to the weird and unsettling phenomenon of perceiving an Effect before its Cause – rather like seeing a glass tumbler shatter before it fell off the table.

Martin Brenton said, 'Aren't we jumping the gun in supposing Chris to be the injectee? I understood the selection date to be some weeks off.'

'So we are and so it is,' Karve said easily, stuffing his pipe with tobacco. His eyes twinkled from beneath ragged grey eyebrows. 'We were speaking hypothetically, Martin. Hypotheses are two a penny around here today.'

After the evening meal Queghan and Milton Blake stood in the grounds watching the more energetic delegates playing tennis and the less athletic having a game of crown green bowls. Small groups sat here and there discussing the day's Papers and debating their importance and possible consequences. Queghan asked Blake about the technique he was working on and whether it would provide – the big question – the predictive capability that everyone was seeking.

Blake considered his reply, the pale palms of his hands cupped as if to catch his thoughts and present them to the listener. 'Everything depends on the sender. I'm sure you realize that, Chris. The display is only the interface between his brain impulses and our perception of them. The problem is that human beings tend to be so erratic in terms of performance and reliability that it would be safer to have the hardware do it for us.'

'There would still be discrepancies,' Queghan pointed out.

'I wouldn't dispute that for a moment. But any discrepancies would come from the sender, from the injectee. We would assume – we would have to assume – any interference in the transfer of information to be caused by difficulties encountered by the sender at the point of transmission.'

Queghan took this in, and then said, 'But the vital question is still the one of predictive capability. Presumably you'd record the sender's mind-waves prior to injection and keep them on master tape as a means of comparison. But what guarantee is there that after injection into Temporal Flux he'll find himself in the spacetime coordinate predicted earlier? His world-point could, quite literally, be anywhere.'

'Or nowhere,' Milton Blake said. He shrugged and dropped his hands. 'The fact is – and we have to face up to it – there is no guarantee. As I said before, everything depends on the sender. If he happens to pass into, either deliberately or inadvertently, a spatio-temporal coordinate other than the one recorded on master tape, then we don't have a cat in hell's chance of locating him. He could be as near to us in terms of displacement as the radius of a proton and we'd never know it. Nor could we ever effect retrieval: he'd be lost and gone forever.'

'It's a bloody fine distinction,' Queghan said. They had come to pause by the perimeter fence, beyond which the encroaching darkness had taken possession.

'And a cruel one. Wherever he found himself, supposing he actually had a physical existence, he'd be trapped for all time. Maybe in the worst of all possible worlds, who knows?'

Queghan laced his fingers into the mesh of the fence. He suddenly needed to feel the physical reality of an actual object; the planet beneath his feet seemed transitory and insubstantial.

He stared into the darkness and said, 'That idea of Johann's. Do you suppose it might be feasible?'

'Which idea was that?'

'The one he mentioned at lunchtime.'

To Queghan's discomposure Blake burst out laughing. His teeth were a vivid crescent in the gloom.

'Is it so preposterous?'

'The idea of transmitting tachyons, you mean?' Blake laughed again and then sobered a little. 'I suppose not,' he said, and then, more seriously, 'I've never given it much consideration. The problems would be tremendous. We can't even isolate tachyons, never mind transmit them. And now I come to think about it, what I said at lunchtime is really the crucial question: how do we know what to ask when we receive the answers first? It'd be like answering the questions in an examination paper before the examiner had set them or even made up his mind what to ask. I suppose, in the cyberthetic sense, there's no reason why it couldn't be made to work, but in practice—?' He shook his head doubtfully

'The chicken and the egg,' Queghan said.

'The egg and the egg.' Blake's face was an anonymous blur above the crisp and dazzling points of his collar. 'Where do we start? Easier to trap fog with this wire fence.'

Queghan said quietly, as if thinking aloud, 'But we do know that tachyons exist. We know – we think we know – they're responsible for precognitive perception.'

'This is more your field than mine,' Milton Blake said. 'I have no extrasensory faculties and don't pretend to have. But I think you'll agree that while we have a theoretical structure for paranormal phenomena it's the very devil of a job to impose a formal scientific code of behaviour on them. For a start, the mathematics don't make sense, they're completely up the wall; but, for some reason God alone knows, they actually work. We don't understand, we simply accept.'

They turned away from the outer darkness and strolled back to the residential quarters. The night was warm and the air dense with the heavy green smell of close-packed shrubbery. There was no moon and it was quite dark.

'You must come and see what we're doing at the Unit,' Milton Blake said. 'You'd find it interesting.'

'Yes, I'm sure. Is the display operational?'

'Has been for three months now. I've been running comparison tests using patients from the Unit – cases we have full data on, EEG records and so forth. We feed the output into the machine and come up with some pretty strange stuff.'

'Fantasies?'

'Fantasies, fetishes, complexes—'

Queghan reached out and steered him round an obstacle, then set him back on the path. As they approached the lighted forecourt Milton Blake said, 'If you're selected, will you go?'

'Yes.'

'No qualms?'

'A few.'

'I suppose if you've been preparing yourself for this one opportunity you can't very well turn it down.'

'That's it.'

'How does Oria feel about your going?'

'She thinks she accepts it.'

'You mean she doesn't accept it?'

'Intellectually yes, emotionally no.'

There were still several small groups sitting close to the anti-mosquito screens, the subdued murmur of voices very restful on the velvet night air.

'Tell me something. I've often wondered about this.' Milton Blake pressed the palms of his hands together. 'How much can you foresee? Is it a hit-or-miss affair, or can you predict with certainty what's going to happen?'

'You mean, do I know for an absolute fact that I'm going to be selected. The answer is no, I don't know. It doesn't work like that. If I made an effort to find out that's the one sure way of never finding out. It has to come to me, to seek me out first.'

'The harder you chase it the faster it outpaces you.'

'Yes.'

Milton Blake went up the steps. 'You must come along to the Unit, Chris. We have more sights there than are dreamt of in your philosophy.'

'I'm sure that's true,' Queghan said, fully intending to visit the Psychic Conservation Unit, more commonly known as PSYCON.

The study was a shambles. It was as if the Director had gone out of his way to foster an image of the amiable eccentric professor pottering about with pipe and slippers amidst the flotsam of academic chaos. Indeed, he did wear slippers and smoke a pipe, but his manner was far from bumbling and he was anything but woolly-minded.

When Queghan entered the room it was like stepping into a peaceful backwater where time ticked by with the measured serenity of a pendulum; yet Johann Karve's gentle appearance and genial disposition were deceiving only to those rash enough to accept anyone or anything at face value. He offered Quegan a cup of tea and, while waiting for the kettle to boil (another apparent 'eccentricity'), they talked generally about the Project and the minutiae of day-to-day administration. But Queghan surmised that this was only a preamble to the main proceedings.

'Karla should be along in a minute or two,' Karve remarked, setting out three cups and saucers. He hummed something tuneless and patted his pockets in a convincing parody of a nuclear physicist having mislaid the vital equation for the Lepton Anti-Matter Bomb.

'You're visiting the, er, Unit soon, I hear,' he said, breaking off his tuneless drone.

'Next week. Milton has a patient he wants me to observe who has the notion he's receiving messages from a parallel universe.'

'Blake receiving messages?' Karve said, pausing with grey eyebrows suspended high on his forehead.

'No,' Queghan smiled. 'The patient.'

'Yes, of course. Parallel universes,' Karve mused. 'How the old SF writers used to love parallel universes.' He poured boiling water into the china teapot and said, 'We've narrowed our potential target areas down to two.'

Queghan watched him without responding.

'Perhaps you know them already.'

'I'll make a guess. Would I be far out if I suggested that our old friend HD226868 is one of them?'

'We've examined a number of single-line spectroscopic binaries and, yes, HD226868 is one of the likely candidates. In the final analysis, however, it depends which is the better suited to accommodate a Dyson Electromagnetic Sphere capable of containing the Temporal Flux radiation.' Karve sat down behind the desk piled several layers deep with files, data processing cards, reels of magnetic tape and a number of thick reference works bristling with markers. There was also a cyberthetic input and a desk-mounted Indexer, tuned, Queghan noted, to alpha.

'And the other candidate?' Queghan said.

'Ah yes.' Karve had drifted away for a moment. 'Yes, the other one is the companion to Theta^2 Orionis in M.42, X-ray reference $2U0525$-06. I think, for what my personal opinion is worth, that this is the one we should go for: its collapsar has a mass similar to the companion of HD226868, about fourteen solar masses, but its orbital period is 21 days as opposed to 5.6 days, which gives us far greater leeway in positioning for injection. It shouldn't be— Come in,' he said in response to Karla Ritblat's knock, the authoritative sound of a person with no time to waste.

Queghan nodded companionably to Karla Ritblat as she made herself briskly comfortable, sitting perfectly straight in the chair ergonomically designed to promote a relaxed posture. Her grey hair, flecked with silver, was cut in the shape of a norman helmet, enclosing her broad, flattish face and tending to emphasize its severity. She said, 'No sugar, thank you.'

'I've been telling Chris about our two target areas, Karla.' The Director leaned back and sipped his tea, holding the cup in both hands as if to warm them. 'However, that's by the way. We'll have a feasibility report within a day or so and that should decide things for us, one way or the other.'

'We've made our preference known, I hope, Director?' Karla Ritblat said, the cup suspended between lip and saucer.

Karve nodded. He let out his breath and said, 'Chris, the purpose of this meeting – at Karla's suggestion by the way – is to finalize the selection procedure. Karla has made the point that whoever's chosen will have to undergo at least six months' preparation in Psycho-Med, not counting the actual pre-injection medical checks, so we have to stop counting sheep and get our—' his gaze wavered momentarily from Queghan's face to Karla Ritblat's '—collective fingers out.'

The woman sat cold and impassive as stone.

'I didn't know there was a race on,' Queghan said.

'There isn't . . . not as such.' The Director seemed unaccountably ill at ease. He drank his tea and then spent some time setting the cup back in the saucer. 'You know that MyTT was given full responsibility for selection, and we've had to consider every conceivable factor: age, medical history, blood type, specialist ability, family background, etc. Well,' he looked directly at Queghan, 'the choice narrowed down to three: Brenton, Castel, yourself.'

Queghan said incredulously, 'Castel?' He looked from one to the other. 'I never knew that.'

Karla Ritblat spoke up. 'If I may say so, Professor Castel is an extremely suitable candidate. Extremely suitable. His IQ and reliability ratings were exceptional.'

'I wouldn't dispute that. It just never occurred to me . . .'

'The point is,' Karve went on, 'that all three of you were screened and each had qualities the other two lacked. Ideally we could have done with the three of you rolled into one, the Ideal Composite Candidate, so to speak.'

Queghan felt strange. He had experienced a distinct and by no means comforting presentiment: he wasn't going to be selected. The instinct was as strong as he had ever known it, an absolute certain conviction . . . and yet, how could this be? His world-line had been fixed, nothing could change it; unless . . .

The Director was speaking again, seeming to confirm Queghan's own worst fears. 'And there's also the factor, not to be lightly considered, of not only who is best suited to go but who we can afford to *let* go. We need a mythographer to interpret the inflow of data through the spatio-temporal interface. We also need a cyberthetics specialist as a backup for the Vehicle herself.'

'But you don't desperately need an archivist,' Queghan said.

'No, that's true,' Karla Riblat said primly. She was looking not at him but at Karve, and with what seemed to be a peculiar expression; Queghan couldn't make it out until he realized she was smiling. He couldn't recall ever having seen such a smile on her face before.

He said: 'What you're trying to tell me is—'

'What we're trying to tell you,' Karve said, 'is that your intuition could be your downfall, Chris.' He, too, was smiling. Queghan was baffled, bewildered, totally lost. 'The decision has been made. Quite frankly, I would have preferred you to remain here with us, working in the TFC Lab, but Karla has the final say in the matter.'

Karla Ritblat said, 'This is off the record, of course, but it was only fair to give you advance notice. We'd like – we would appreciate – your decision within seventy-two hours.'

'Yes,' Queghan said. He was at a loss to say anything else.

'Your wife is expecting a child, I believe?'

'Yes,' Queghan said.

Karve said, 'There's no reason why the official announcement couldn't be held over until after the baby is born. If you think that might help.'

'It would help. Thank you. I thought . . .'

'Yes?' Karve made a prism of his hands and looked over it with that keen, shaggy-browed gaze that gave the lie to his pretence of a bumbling professor.

'I was under the impression that the selection date was a couple of weeks away. I know that Brenton is very keen to be chosen. Does he know of the decision?'

'That, Chris, is the reason for this meeting today. We know how Martin feels, which is why we need your decision. If you should decline, then Martin is the second choice; but he need never know that. It would be bad psychologically. Karla suggested we talk to you first, with no obligation on your part, and if you say no we can make the announcement as planned.'

'And Brenton would be the one.'

'Yes.'

'He thinks the Vehicle won't be compatible with anyone else.'

'We're aware of that,' Karla Ritblat said. 'It will be taken care of during Psycho-Med preparation. It's a matter of programming, that's all, nothing we can't overcome. Within three months it'll seem as though you're married to the Vehicle.'

'I hope Brenton won't feel cuckolded,' Queghan said.

*

93

Milton Blake was glad to see Queghan and showed him round the Unit, a square two-storey building with clinical white walls and rotating pyramids of blue-tinted glass on the roof which caught and reflected triangles of light; from a distance the building appeared to be signalling in broken morse code. Against the hard glare of the white wall the name *PSYCON* stood in black-lettered relief and, beneath it, in smaller script: Faculty of MetaPsychical Research.

'Like everyone else we're fighting for more money,' Blake said, stepping aside to let Queghan through the door into the transmission area. 'We've put together a prototype but, as you'll see, it's held together by chewing gum and sealing wax. The 3D display is actually something we've borrowed from the astro-technology people.'

'What about the neuron processing equipment?'

'Cyberthetic,' Blake said, stepping over a coil of multi-coloured cables as thick as a man's thigh which snaked across the vinyl floor. He edged round a bank of instrumentation, its open guts a maze of solid-state circuitry. 'We have a permanent on-line link-up which handles the processing and gives us direct feedback. Then we do our bit of jiggery-pokery and up it comes on the display, large as life and twice as ugly.'

'Do you have a name for the system?'

Milton Blake smiled in the easy unaffected way only people confident of their attractive appearance can. Queghan felt pale, tall and ghostly beside him. 'We do have several names for it, most of them four-letter ones. Usually it's referred to as NELLIE by the staff, but it's registered in the catalogue as a Neuron Processing & Transfer/Three-Dimensional Display Interface.'

'Wow,' Queghan said.

'Try making an acronym out of that.'

'I won't even attempt it,' Queghan said, looking round the transmission area. It wasn't very large, every cubic metre utilized for some purpose or other, even the ceiling, from which hung tangled skeins of wiring bound together with tape. It looked a mess – though prototype hardware, as Queghan knew only too well, just growed and growed with a seemingly haphazard accumulation of electro-mechanical junk. 'I don't see the display,' he said.

'Up there.' Blake pointed to an angled observation plate high in one corner. 'We watch the display in the box, a separate viewing room, and keep an eye on the patient at the same time. It wouldn't do if he woke up and saw his own nightmares made flesh.'

Queghan was surprised. 'Is that possible? I assumed he'd be heavily sedated during transmission.'

'Sedated yes, but not heavily. If we put him too far under we get a blank screen; it kills everything but the snores.'

He took Queghan along to the Psychiatric Wing where four patients had private rooms and their own medical team. They were well cared for and had agreed voluntarily to take part in the neuron processing experiment.

Blake explained: 'They're all psychiatric cases, ranging from mild neurosis to manic-depressive paranoia. The case in Room Three is the one I'd like you to observe; he claims to be in contact with a parallel universe – in fact during transmission he believes himself to be *in* a parallel universe. It's absolutely real to him.'

'And when he's conscious?' Queghan asked.

'As far as we can make out his few waking moments are a sort of dreamworld. He talks to the staff as though they're part of this other place; he's got his own private alternative universe.'

'So we're the dream, the other place is the reality.'

'That's it.'

'He might just have a point.'

Milton Blake laughed. 'You're here to observe, but I'm sure we could find a bed for you.' He gave instructions that the patient in Room Three (a hollow-eyed, emaciated fellow called Stahl) should be prepared, then took Queghan along to the viewing room, overlooking the transmission area. Through the tangle of wires and other paraphernalia they saw the patient being wheeled in and positioned like a white oblong chess piece amid the clutter of equipment.

'We put him under an hour ago, ready for transmission. We can regulate his dream cycle through to Stage IV; then we hold him there, and when we're ready an implant triggers the brain chemical acetylcholine, and then we wait for the rhythm peaks to reach optimum. Which doesn't take long,' he added, reaching forward to adjust the controls on the three-dimensional display.

Queghan said, 'From which viewpoint do we observe the patient's fantasies – through his own eyes and perceptions, or objectively, as an onlooker?'

'Both,' Blake said. His hands were expressive as he explained: 'Sometimes we observe from the patient's viewpoint, and at others we see the patient himself, inside his dream, as it were. Think of your own dreams as a neurological landscape. Most of the time you're aware of being an entity, an individual person looking out at what's happening, seeing the dream subjectively. At other times it's as though you're watching the scene from no particular place, almost like a disembodied presence, and you can watch yourself – knowing it's you – reacting to the dream.'

Queghan wanted to know if the dream always followed a logical sequence, as a story in a movie.

'Stahl usually begins with the same scene, as though he's tuning in by using the same image, and it follows on from there. We get interference, of course, fragmentary bits and pieces which don't fit in anywhere, but there is a logic to it, though sometimes it's pretty weird. Anyway, you'll see for yourself.'

Somebody down below spoke through the talkback: a woman's voice. 'Professor Blake, the patient is showing REM activity. Shall we boost the signal?'

'One moment, Zandra,' Blake said, fiddling with the controls. The display remained blank, a muddy ochre. 'What have we on the cyberthetic input readout?'

'It's on-line, Professor. You should be getting something.'

'REM,' Queghan said. 'Rapid Eye Movement?'

Blake nodded, still intent on the controls, and said, 'Take it up slowly; don't overload the circuit or he'll have a nightmare,' and then, his voice rising, 'Yes, we're getting something.' He glanced through the observation plate to the patient below, and even from this distance it was possible to see the flutter of the eyelids indicating a dreaming state. The display had cleared, a vista appearing through mist, the muddy ochre replaced by a brilliant sparkling red laced here and there with streaks of purple.

'Ah,' Blake said with evident satisfaction, as a conjurer performing his best trick, 'there we have it: the red ocean.'

'A red ocean?' Queghan said after a pause.

Blake leaned back after sharpening the focus, not moving his eyes from the display. 'This is Stahl's tuning-in point. He might continue from here or jump to a later incident.'

'He's projected this scene before?'

'It's never quite the same. There are always minor discrepancies, things left out or new things added, details changed, and so on. Maybe it's caused by a neurochemical imbalance at the time of transmission, we really don't know.' He was like someone settling down to watch his favourite video program.

'I suppose we don't have sound,' Queghan said, not entirely serious, but Blake took the question at face value.

'We're working on that. Maybe on our second generation module; but sound has problems, as you'll know if you think about your own dreams for a moment. They're primarily a visual medium.'

Queghan wanted to ensure there was no possibility of error, no margin for misunderstanding: 'What we're seeing on the display are the patient's neurological impulses which have been processed cyberthetically and transferred into visual wavelengths.'

'On the button,' Milton Blake said, intent on the screen.

Queghan's first impression was that the image was remarkably lifelike. The red ocean rippled beneath a huge yellow sun, the waves peaked with purple foam dashed against something below the line of vision and exploded in a translucent rainbow – a rainbow in which all the colours were shifted towards the red. It seemed that the patient (this was Queghan's thought) had projected himself into a world with an exceptionally powerful gravitational field; either that or the planet was moving at a velocity approaching that of lightspeed. Nothing else, to his knowledge, could account for the red shift.

The eye-view swept the horizon as if seeking a point of reference, found none, and came to rest on a pair of feet encased in a black shiny ribular substance resembling seared thermoplastic.

'What is he floating on?'

'Some kind of metal dish. The last time he transmitted this sequence it went on for five hours.'

As he spoke the scene shivered and they caught a confused glimpse of the man himself, gaunt to the point of pale death, his eyes sunk deep in their sockets: it was, and yet strangely wasn't, the patient lying below in the transmission area. It was the patient as seen through a distorting mirror, the features twisted out of shape and the prominences showing through like bleached bone.

Again the image trembled: the yellow sun against a backdrop of deepest azure filled the frame and vibrated like a pulsing eye so that Queghan could almost feel the heat crinkling his flesh and evaporating the moisture in the pores of his scalp. It was too fierce, too real; he was intimidated by the realness of it.

Blake said: 'We should see the ship any minute now. The ocean, the seizure, the ship, that's the usual pattern . . .' but for Queghan this was, and he recognized it as such, a mythic experience. Blake saw it as an interesting experiment, but Queghan's gift of instinctive apprehension awoke in him a mystical feelings, whereby the leys of the universe had been revealed – a finite, irreducible grain of truth laid bare. He began to lose track of himself as a kind of floating airiness overcame his senses. It was as though the range and breadth of his perceptions had increased by a factor of ten – a flash of light in the brain – and the sense of life, the consciousness of self, expanded within him so that all his vital forces were working at their highest tension. The past and future ages of man became a comprehensible whole: there was a grand design which he was on the edge of perceiving, and he knew beyond doubt that everything had meaning – from the world-within-world of submicroscopic processes to the ultra-macroscopic vastness of galaxies moving on their predestined paths through the universe. There was cosmic harmony, and everything, animate and inanimate, was a vital and necessary part.

*

'Do you think NELLIE has a future?' Milton Blake said.

'In respect of the Project?'

'That's what I had in mind.'

'Yes, there's no question,' Queghan said slowly. He had not yet returned to the everyday world of common sense and causality; his eyes lingered on the blank display for a moment. 'I think in fact that the applications are wider than we had anticipated. What you have here could make a tremendous contribution to Myth Technology, in particular to our applied-research program. There are certain repositories of knowledge contained in ancient myths and legends: we are our own myth-makers, and we unconsciously create legends and symbols which express hidden truths.'

'The leys,' Blake said, smiling. 'I've read up on some of the jargon you mythographers use.'

'The leys themselves are the links which connect the areas of truth and beauty, harmony and order throughout the Meta-galaxy. We perceive them only randomly, and when we do we rarely understand their true meaning. But with this' – he indicated the display – 'we can conjure up visually our deepest, most intuitive, most elusive feelings; we can record and study and interpret.'

'The display makes no distinction between reality, memory, myth or fantasy,' Blake pointed out.

'Perhaps there is no distinction,' Queghan said. 'Among the many meanings of the word "fantasy" you'll find the definition "a visionary idea or speculation". We are in the business of pursuing visionary ideas and speculations and trying to understand them.'

'You think the red ocean has a mythic quality?'

'I'm positive that it has,' Queghan answered. 'The vessel that rescued him from the ocean, the captain and crew, the experiment in the sanatorium, the airship taking him to the concentration camp, are all glimpses of a mythical world which is just as valid as our own.'

'Even though imaginary—'

'*Even* though?' Queghan said. 'Even though what? The reversal of causality and the dynamics of probability point to the fact that imaginary planes of existence have equal validity with anything we can physically detect with our senses and our instruments. We know by observation that the Metagalaxy ought to contain perhaps ten times as much matter as it appears to contain; we are part of the observable ten per cent, so in point of fact we're the minor portion*. The bulk of it is hidden from us, and to that other, greater part of the Metagalaxy, wherever it is to be found, *we* are the imaginary missing piece.'

Blake looked down through the observation plate at the patient, now calm and bathed in sweat. The medical staff were removing the apparatus connected to his head.

He said, 'Without entirely disputing what you say, Chris, I think Stahl has borrowed rather than invented or conjured up some of the material. For one thing, he believes he's being held in a place called Psy-Con, when it's clear to me that he's simply transferred the name of the PSYCON Unit into his fantasy.'

'Did it ever occur to you that the reverse might be true?' Queghan said. 'Perhaps he transposed Psy-Con into PSYCON.'

'Yes,' Milton Blake said slowly, looking at Queghan.

The theory positing the existence of Temporal Flux Centres was by no means new or revolutionary: it had a long and involved scientific history stretching back to Pre-Colonization times. It had been in the year 1798 (Gregorian calendar) that the French mathematician Pierre Laplace, using Newton's theory of gravitation as the basis for his calculations, had forecast that a body above a certain critical mass and density would prevent light escaping from its surface and would therefore be invisible to any outside observer. With his equations in the early part of the twentieth century, Einstein came forward with conclusive proof that a body of such mass and density was not only possible but mathematically inevitable.

Then in 1916 (Gc), Karl Schwarzschild, working on the relativistic principle of spacetime distortion, calculated the criti-

* For further information the reader is referred to the work carried out by Professor J. A. Wheeler, as summarized in his book *Geometrodynamics* (Academic Press, 1962).

cal radius of an extremely small, extremely massive spherical object – such as a White Dwarf – and arrived at a set of equations which could be used to define this radius for any object, no matter how large or small. This became known as the Schwarzschild Radius*, and, once having achieved it, an object would distort spacetime so severely that nothing could ever escape from it. The sun of Old Earth, for example, with a radius of 700,000 kilometres, would have to be compressed to a radius of three kilometres before it achieved Temporal Flux – or as it was known in the early days of discovery – a 'Black Hole'.

For many years Pre-Colonization, the existence of Black Holes was a matter for speculation and controversy. The main problem was how to locate a body which emitted no radiation of any kind and was totally invisible to observers using visual and electromagnetic sensing equipment. Two methods were postulated as a means of detecting these elusive creatures: the measurement of gravitational radiation and the single-line spectroscopic binary system. Joseph Weber of the Princeton Institute for Advanced Study was the first, with his Paper *Gravitational Radiation Experiments* published in 1970 (Gc), to claim an experimental result which might confirm the existence of Temporal Flux Centres in the denser parts of the Milky Way galaxy. Synchronized instruments placed 600 miles apart had detected short violent bursts of gravitational energy – so violent that the only explanation was that entire stars were being sucked into and swallowed by Temporal Flux Centres, their abrupt extinction being accompanied by a burst of radiation many millions of times more powerful than could be accounted for by any other known phenomenon in the universe.

The evidence provided by a study of single-line spectroscopic binary systems was even more conclusive. In the latter part of the twentieth century detailed and systematic observation showed that of the binary (double star) systems, a number possessed invisible companions, which were detectable by the influence they exerted on the visible star. Some of these companions, on further investigation, turned out to be old dead

* See Appendix II.

stars or, as in the case of Sirius B in Alpha Canis Majoris, White Dwarfs. But a significant proportion were found to possess invisible companions of sufficient mass and density to fit the category of Temporal Flux Centre, notably HD226868, Theta^2 Orionis in M.42, Epsilon Aurigae lying close to Capella, and the eclipsing binary Beta Lyrae near the brilliant blue star Vega.

This was the foundation upon which the subsequent study of Temporal Flux Centres was based. It progressed theoretically but languished in practice in Pre-Colonization times because of man's inability to escape the Solar System. It required – it depended upon – the development of interstellar travel, which took four centuries to achieve. The breakthrough was prosaic, almost archaic, for it was the rediscovery of the work done by an obscure English electrical engineer in the nineteenth century, Oliver Heavyside, which finally led, almost by accident, to a modification of Einsteinian physics.

It was a basic tenet of Einstein's Special Theory of Relativity that nothing possessing mass can exceed lightspeed; by employing the Heavyside formulae, which dealt with the interaction of electromagnetic waves and gravitational energy, it was shown that this rule didn't apply when the force of gravitation was balanced out, or negated, by the action of electromagnetic pulses of energy. In a real sense, it made precise use of the Einsteinian concept of *relativity* – ironically turning it against itself – for if nothing could exceed lightspeed and yet lightspeed itself was relative (depending on the point of reference from which it was being observed) then it followed that while lightspeed could not be exceeded in a local frame of reference, in cosmic terms the absolute velocity of lightspeed had no meaning: it was a variable factor*. The Galaxy, relative to other galaxies, was moving beyond lightspeed, and, once a method could be found to 'break out' of the local frame of reference, then interstellar travel would evolve to a problem of technology.

This 'breaking out' was achieved by a rupturing of four-

* In fact, Einstein allowed for this in proposing that lightspeed was affected by gravitational fields of energy.

dimensional spacetime – a concept impossible to visualize – which could only be expressed mathematically. To students it was explained as being analogous to a race of people living on a videovision screen. Imagine, they were told, that these people had only two dimensions – length and breadth, but no depth – and whose world is totally confined to this flat two-dimensional plane. They have no knowledge of 'roundness', they are thin, flat creatures who have no idea that a third dimension exists. But we, as outside observers, can see clearly that a third dimension *does* exist in which it is possible to move around. Further imagine, they were asked, these flatlanders to be living on a sphere: they can move forwards or backwards, to left or right, but not up or down. If they decide to travel along the surface of their sphere (to them it will appear completely flat) they will travel on for ever, believing themselves to be in an endless universe. Now if we transfer this concept of a two-dimensional world to our three-dimensional one, we can understand, if not visualize, a fourth dimension which our senses are incapable of detecting. We are in a sense three-dimensional 'flatlanders' existing in a four-dimensional universe. And just as the two-dimensional people travelling round their sphere will eventually arrive back where they started from, so we, heading deeper into the Metagalaxy, will eventually arrive back at our starting point.

This schoolboy analogy was complicated by the dynamics of spacetime curvature. As predicted by Einstein's gravitational field equations, spacetime was not an absolute uniform medium permeating all of Creation, but was affected – 'wrinkled' or 'curved' – by the presence of bodies embedded in it. Planets moved in orbit round the sun not because the sun attracted them (as in the Newtonian model of gravitation) but because the spacetime curvature exerted by the sun's presence confined the motion of planets to a circular world-line. In spacetime curvature, these circular motions were represented by geodesics which, paradoxically, showed that the shortest distance between two points was not a straight line but a curved one.

This same work, almost incidentally, provided the theoretical evidence for the existence of Temporal Flux Centres, for when a body of immense mass and density collapsed beyond the Schwarzschild Radius it distorted surrounding spacetime to such an extent that the curvature was total; spacetime folded in upon itself and formed a 'singularity' – the structure of matter was annihilated in a region of infinite spacetime curvature. And just as planets followed their world-lines round the sun (a relatively gentle effect of spacetime curvature), so the particles of energy and matter in a Temporal Flux Centre were subject to the curvature of spacetime in its most devastating and obliterating form.

The work of Heavyside, which had lain dormant for centuries, was amazingly apposite when applied to the problem of how to overcome the limiting factor of lightspeed. His particular passion had been for electromagnetism – a new and unexplored field in his day – which seemed only remotely linked to relativistic physics, the great crowning glory of scientific achievement in the twentieth century. Yet it was Heavyside who laid down the principle of 'electromagnetic interference' (EMI), whereby gravitational energy could be diverted or controlled, creating not so much an anti-gravity field as a change in its astro-physical properties. This in itself was exciting but not significant – until one brought in the concept of spacetime curvature and the varying speed of light in a gravitational field. If one could control gravity by means of an electromagnetic force, then it must follow that lightspeed was also capable of manipulation. Interstellar distances, which were indeed vast, could be conquered, not by travelling across them in the conventional sense, but by *relativistically reducing the distance to be travelled*. It was the classic case of bringing the mountain to Mohammed: moving the destination closer (ie varying the factor of lightspeed) so that the time it took to travel there was shorter.

This introduced a new branch of astro-technology, because it soon became evident that interstellar vehicles didn't require propulsion units, nuclear, chemical or any other type. In fact they didn't require anything. It was only necessary to place the vehicle in a field of electromagnetic interference, set the spatio-temporal coordinates, and press the button. For practical purposes, the field was created in deep space in a quiet and uncluttered part of the Solar System. This was to reduce the radiation hazard and also to prevent accidents: anything inside the field would be transported to the destination, and, if set up on earth, would have meant the staff and laboratory going along for the ride too, whatever their personal feelings or preferences.

The beauty and utter simplicity of the EMI Field, from the astro-technologists' point of view, was that lightspeed, far from limiting their technical capability as had once been feared, actually became the key which opened the door to interstellar travel. Without this 'golden mean' they would have had to resort to such tedious methods as those of suspended animation or 'generation' space vessels as huge as several ocean liners, or some fanciful invention like 'hyperdrive', beloved of SF writers of the era Pre-Colonization. In fact it was amusing to look back to those times and read of the devious, almost perverse ways in which both scientists and fiction writers sought to overcome the 'insurmountable' problem of faster-than-light travel. Their mistake was in treating it as a barrier, an impasse somehow to be avoided, when all along it was an ally: lightspeed itself was the answer staring them in the face.

And now a new step in cosmic exploration was about to be taken. Man was preparing to enter that region of the Metagalaxy existing alongside, or even within, the observable universe. It was there, it existed, of that there could be no doubt: the Hidden Universe where the laws of space and time, energy and matter, were changed beyond recognition. The way in – the only way – was via the one-way membrane of a Temporal Flux Centre; and man was about to take the first step.

The image transmitted by Stahl had profoundly disturbed him. It contained all the elements of a genuine mythoplasm: a composite of myth, legend and psychic projection. To Stahl, the universe he had created was more real than Room Three of the Psychic Conservation Unit where his physical presence was located; subjective reality was a world of red oceans, airships and concentration camps where millions of people were held in captivity. Supposing they were to inject Stahl into Temporal

Flux – would he find himself inhabiting his private fantasy, trapped in a world of his own nightmarish imaginings? Queghan recalled a line from Karve's *The Hidden Universe*: 'The universe is nothing until we think of it in a certain way; it is an expression of how we ourselves perceive it.' What would his perceptions be, having once passed beyond the event horizon into the maelstrom of Temporal Flux? Did hell, complete with all its demons, await him there?

Oria was sitting in the garden, her body bathed golden by the rays of the sun. There was another chair near by, and Queghan noticed that it still retained the shape of a recent sitter in the contoured vinyl. (The stranger of his dreams, perhaps, having dematerialized on Queghan's arrival?)

He kissed her and said, 'Pregnancy agrees with you.'

'Was PSYCON worth the trip?' There were faint vertical marks of tension on her forehead, as if she had acquired a slight though permanent frown.

'It was . . . interesting.'

'Will it help the Project?'

'Perhaps.'

'You're being evasive,' Oria said, laying her book down. Queghan read the title upside down: *The First Year of Motherhood*.

'No, it's really too soon to say. The equipment is in prototype. The results so far are certainly interesting, but I shall have to discuss it with Johann before making any kind of recommendation'.

He sat down, re-shaping the chair to his form, and closed his eyes; the sun glimmered redly behind his eyelids and he was reminded of the ocean.

'What's the temperature of the fluid at the moment of transfusion?' Oria asked.

Queghan opened one eye. 'The temperature . . .'

'Of the fluid. The injectee receives a complete transfusion of fluid to preserve the molecular structure.'

'How do you know about that?'

'I was in Archives for three years,' Oria reminded him. 'I read up on the Psycho-Med preparations prior to injection.'

'Was that before or after you revised the general theory of relativity?' Queghan closed his eye again. 'So why do you want to know the transfusion temperature?'

'Do you think it might be similar to giving birth?'

'There's no way I'm ever going to be able to answer that,' Queghan said, grinning into the sun. He was trying to register her but there was too much emotional static, too many impulses scurrying about like blind mice chasing their own tails. He would like to have slept for a long time, the sun held in suspension above the trees, the sun chosen as beneficent provider by a technocratic race. God had created man in His own image and man had created worlds in his own image. God the Creator of the Metagalaxy, man its shaper. How far did they have to go before the mystery revealed itself? And what would they find at the end of it – a tired old man sitting in a shabby cobwebbed room watching the endless sinking of the sun?

Oria was crying. She said, 'I don't want to lose you.'

He said, almost with relief, 'I thought it was the child; I thought something had happened to the child.'

'The child is all right.' The tears fell on to her distended breasts, rolled and evaporated into thin, dried trails.

Queghan went to her, holding both her hands. 'Nothing will be left to chance, you know how careful they are. Johann won't give the word until he's one hundred per cent certain that every system is at optimum.'

'A hundred per cent certain of a fifty per cent probability,' Oria said. Her pale-blue eyes shimmered through the refraction of her tears. 'You didn't have to accept, Chris. Brenton wanted to go, he'd risk anything, he's not married, it didn't matter to him.'

There should have been something he could have said, some magical phrase that would make everything all right, but the magical phrase eluded him. He said emptily, like a child making excuses, 'You said I had no alternative.'

'It didn't matter then, it was unreal, it wasn't you, it was some other person we were discussing. The real you would still be here: this make-believe person would be going, not you.'

'There may be a million mythical futures but there's only one me, I'm afraid,' he said, attempting to smile.

'Chris,' Oria said softly, 'Chris, there's no way back. They can inject you into that place, wherever it is, but they can never bring you back. You know it, that's why you didn't tell me, you know that you'll never return . . .'

Queghan saw her for a split second, absolutely cold-bloodedly, as a neurochemical organism responding to electrical stimuli, as a body secreting warm salty fluid, as a mammalian receptacle for the furtherance of the species. He thought: we have come so far and still a woman's tears defeat us; defeat our science, our logic, our knowledge. What is the point of anything when a commonplace emotion can reduce us to helplessness? If we don't understand this, what do we understand? And what is the point of understanding anything?

'Who told you? Johann was going to withhold the announcement until after the baby was born.'

'The baby,' Oria said. 'The fucking baby!' She raised her fists as if to strike him and hit herself in the stomach very hard. Queghan caught her wrists and held them, like brittle sparrow's bones in his large hands. She had amazing strength and he had to hold her in a tight grip, afraid that in wanting to harm the child she would kill them both.

Anger rose up suddenly within him and he said roughly, 'Who was it? Who told you? *Who told you?*'

'Brenton,' she said, the fight and strength gone out of her. He released her wrists. 'Why didn't you tell me, Chris? You should have told me.'

'I would have told you, after the baby came.' A fleck of foam had appeared at the corner of his mouth. 'We agreed, Johann and I agreed, to wait just a few weeks. It wouldn't have made any difference, to the Project, to me, to Brenton—'

'Let him go, Chris,' Oria said. 'Let *him* go. He wants to go. He'd do anything.' She was pale and dry eyed, trying to do by reason what could not be done by emotion. 'They need you here, Brenton said so. He said the Vehicle would reject you—'

'I have to go.'

'Only because you want to go,' she said harshly.

'I have to.' His eyelids fluttered. He felt the world recede, and experienced the glare of white light in his brain, like the flash of a prolonged explosion going on for ever. He tried to say something, but his tongue was coiled thickly in his mouth. The foam bubbled on his lips.

'Chris,' Oria said. '*Chris!*' and failed to hold him as he fell on to the grass, his blank eyeballs staring at the sky, and in the infinitesimal fraction of time before blackness came he heard her voice calling to him, loud and then soft, loud and soft, as he sank into the warm bowels of the planet.

She knelt on the grass, her belly-burden wedged between her thighs. It was like trying to comfort a statue. The sun had disappeared behind the trees, a few lingering rays touching the highest branches, just as the larger of the two moons was rising palely in the northern sky."

6

Psy-Con

'It's simply a matter of Logik,' Benson said. 'Where's your training, old man? Approach the thing logikally and there shouldn't be any problem.' Then he had the gall to smile.

His smile, his confidence, his smugness, his height – above all, his height – infuriated Dr Mathew Black. He was even more incensed to learn that Benson had been sent as Special Envoy, appointed by King's Commission, to review the screening procedure at Psy-Con. Benson had been nothing in the sanatorium, *nothing*, a mere pip-squeak, a jackanapes, and here he was, with power and overall responsibility handed to him on a plate. While he, Black, had been saddled with a babbling madman fit only for the High Intensity Complex. He felt like murdering them both.

'I suppose you would have disposed of the patient and filed your report by now.'

'You've had weeks, old chap,' Benson said, raising his eyebrows yet retaining a trace of a smile. 'The MDA were generous enough to permit an extension, but even that doesn't appear to have satisfied you.' He added as an afterthought, 'And that's something else the Authority will have to answer for.'

There had been another purge. It made Black sick to think about it. The rules were changed, the priorities switched, the Authority restructured, yet again. Cases would be reclassified according to a new set of criteria, the medikal jargon re-interpreted and redrafted to embrace a different code of ethiks. The guards, of course, remained.

'And I thought you were one of our best people,' Benson said condescendingly, shaking his head from side to side.

Black nearly exploded. Our best people! *Our* best people! He had to turn away to the window to hide hs emotion, looking out blindly at the baked landscape and plumes of dust – red, brown, orange, yellow – swirling in the hot wind. This was the pitiless Pilbara, separated from any decent human habitation by several hundred miles of desert and raw scrubland. The roof of the hut in which they were standing was hot enough to evaporate water at a touch, had anyone been foolish enough to squander it in this way.

Benson leaned over the trestle-table and turned a page of the report, which stuck damply to his thin fingers. Everything about him was thin, from his bare spindly legs to his bare bony arms and shoulders and the stringbean of a neck with its jutting Adam's apple. His sun helmet with its King's Commission insignia reminded Black of a bucket balanced on a flagpole. He resisted the urge to laugh.

'You don't seriously expect me to submit this do you?' Benson said, frittering through the pages. 'This nonsense. I should have said HIC classification and got rid of the fellow. What are you trying to prove, some new-fangled theory of diagnosis that'll get your name in the medikal books?' His bulging eyes looked up from the report and compelled Black to turn and meet them.

Black said, somewhat rashly, 'I suppose that's the new order of the day, classify everyone HIC and have done.'

'Not at all, old chap, not at all.' Benson was unexpectedly fraternal. He was so sure of himself that he could afford to be lax about protocol, to be expansive, even. Black was enviously eating himself away. He moved his veiled eyes and looked once more through the window. The dust plumes obscured the horizon. This heat must affect the brain, it must send men mad.

'You tried galvanology, I see,' Benson said, wiping his hands on his handkerchief.

'Yes,' Black said without turning his head.

'Was it a success?'

'It's all there in the report.'

'I asked you if—'

'I think so. But I had to discontinue the experiment. The MDA don't believe in galvanology.'

'Didn't believe.'

'You mean they do now?'

'Considering it, considering it,' Benson said slowly, turning the pages. He had adopted the mannerisms of power and authority with infuriating ease.

'Do I take that to mean I'll be allowed to continue the experiment?'

'Possibly,' Benson drawled. 'Possibly.' He straightened up. 'I conducted some experiments myself in galvanology, as you may recall. Nothing quite so elaborate, but I fancy the results were equally valid.'

A nasty suspicion had entered Black's mind. Benson wanted to take over the patient himself. He had tumbled to the importance of the work Black was engaged on and had decided to step in and take the credit for himself. They would see about that. The nerve of the man – of this long streak of nothing with as much savvy as the rasp of a dry fart.

'I got the impression that you weren't keen on the report,' Black said, a shade too smugly for his own good.

'Some of it I find interesting; mildly interesting.' (I'll bet, thought Black.) 'The patient is obviously at the mercy of a chaotic imagination quite beyond his control. He invents people, events, other worlds even, willy-nilly. He even refers' – Benson turned several pages – 'to another patient, fellow by the name of Stahl, who by some tomfoolery or other finds himself in *this* world, adrift on the ocean.'

'The explanation is very simple. The patient was himself discovered in the ocean and he's unconsciously incorporated the experience into his ramblings. He's done the same with Psy-Con, which has become PSYCON in his imagination. It's very obvious.'

'And the other similarities?'

'What others?' Black said sharply.

'Why, the names of course.' Benson tapped the page with his bony knuckles. 'He mentions someone called Blake, a name similar to your own. There's also a fellow called Brenton, which

112

I take to be a reference to myself. This chap Q is living in two quite separate worlds simultaneously, one of which is imaginary.'

'I could have told you that.'

'Don't be stroppy,' Benson said, glancing up. 'I needn't remind you of your position here. As Special Envoy I have complete authority over all activities in or pertaining to Psy-Con. The patient Q is under my jurisdiction. Strictly speaking, your duties are now discharged. I could have you sent back on the next airship or seconded to the High Intensity Complex.'

'But I'm a qualified doktor attached to the Medikal Centre,' Black protested hotly. 'I'm not here on permanent loan.'

'You will go where I say you must go and do what I say you must do,' Benson told him crisply, his Adam's apple bobbing in his skinny throat. A drop of perspiration gathered on the tip of his nose and fell on to the page. 'As for the patient, I suggest you continue the Gestalt Treatment under my supervision. When the report is complete we can put it forward jointly; I think that's fair enough.'

Black couldn't trust himself to speak; he could barely nod, too furious and sick at heart to do anything else. He prayed that there would be another purge. He wanted to see Benson suffer. He would like to have seen him bitten by a two-headed King snake and his yellow shrunken corpse thrown into the alligator pits.

The inmates were allowed to wander freely within the wire enclosure, though for most of the day it was too hot to venture outside the huts. Inside, it was like a Turkish bath, while outside was an open-hearth furnace. Along with two hundred other newly-arrived deportees, Q was herded into F Compound, one of the twenty or so pre-screening compounds; they were a mixed bunch of both sexes and all ages, several of them under twelve years of age. One of the women was with child.

They were fed twice a day, morning and evening and, in between, there was nothing to do except lie on the bunks and run with sweat. A few made paltry attempts at conversation, but the heat eventually overcame all activity, even that of moving the tongue and mouth to produce sounds. It was as if the brain had gone flaccid, like a heavy decomposing sponge resting on the cranial nerves. Water was strictly rationed, one cupful of warm brackish liquid with each portion of food. The children were allowed half-a-cupful each.

Escape was never discussed, nor even mentioned, because it was plainly impossible: there was nowhere to escape to. Outside the compound lay the desert, and beyond that the sea. These people were here for ever; perhaps the odd one might return to civilization, but he or she would be altered beyond all recognition. And for those who, after screening, would find themselves committed to the High Intensity Complex there was no hope whatsoever. The journey was one way, deeper into the burning hinterland.

Towards sunset a sluggish movement would manifest itself as the inmates drifted from the huts into the faint stirring of air, hardly a breeze, which merely shifted the heat from the desert into the compound. But, with the day advanced, it was fractionally cooler, bearable enough to walk on the ground without blistering the feet. The guards usually waited till after the sun had set before issuing food – not for the benefit of the inmates but because it was less arduous for them, carrying the slop and ladling it into the waiting wooden bowls. Anyone not in the queue didn't receive any food.

Afterwards, in the fast falling darkness, there was the sound of slurping and grunting as everyone sucked the bowls dry, crunching to fragments whatever bones they happened to find. It was sustenance of a kind, just enough to keep body and soul together. And sometimes there were other sounds – cries and frantic scramblings – as one of the guards, for a bit of amusement, threw a snake over the wire and watched it wriggle among the close-packed bodies before being stamped to death in the red earth. It was a harmless diversion at the end of the day, good spectator-sport for the three or four guards who stood laughing outside the perimeter fence. On other nights they might decide to prolong their pleasure, swaggering into the compound and selecting one of the younger females and raping her in full view of the other inmates. If she protested they would beat her with wooden sticks; providing they didn't kill her, anything was permitted.

With the fall of darkness, and the guards retired for the night, the inmates would gather in small groups, sitting cross-legged or slumped in the dust, conversing in low murmurs and perhaps bartering the few meagre possessions they had managed to conceal. The talk was mostly of the past: no one was willing or prepared to visualize a future which they knew to be, though hardly conceivable, worse than the present.

Q was accepted as just another inmate. His peculiar paleness – even more noticeable in this blistering climate – aroused no comment or curiosity. He sat with the others, listening to their reminiscences, now and then prompting them when their stories seemed fragmentary or incomplete. His own past was still largely a mystery to him. He could remember parts of it, dimly realized, as though perceived in dreams, but these dreams were insubstantial scraps which seemed distorted, as if viewed at immense distances through clouds of whirling gas. At other times a revelation crystallized complete in his head, usually a piece of knowledge or information which arrived out of nowhere, so that he knew its most intricate detail, except how it had got there. The thought occurred to him that it might be a religious vision, that he was a prophet of the coming Messiah. But he also knew that if he revealed the thought it would only confirm – to his fellow inmates as much as to Black – that he was truly insane.

In the warm pressing darkness the people sat huddled in groups, talking quietly. Above them the stars were like beacons, huge and near enough to touch, filling the sky to every horizon.

'In New Amerika, so they say, the King has ordered a purge,' someone was saying – a woman in her thirties with thick glossy black hair tied back with grimy ribbon.

'What happens in New Amerika needn't bother you,' said a man's tired voice. 'You are here, my friend. There could be fifty purges and you'd still be here.'

'The King might grant a pardon. It has been known.'

'Has it? I've never heard of it. You're living in daydreams.

*

Better give up hope now, then you won't be doubly disappointed later on.'

'There has been a purge,' someone else said, a young man in his early twenties. 'It was on the telegraph.'

'How do you know what was on the telegraph?' the man scoffed.

'I heard the guards discussing it. They said a message had been received direct from King Jimmy K himself; they said it would affect everyone but them. They were laughing about it.'

'Purges come and purges go,' said the man. 'We stay here for ever.'

A middle-aged woman sitting a little apart from the group said, 'My family are making representations to Court. They've hired a lawyer and an advocate.'

'Is that so,' the man said dryly.

'The lawyer has discovered an edict, an ancient one, which prohibits deportation for any person if more than two members of their family have been on active duty in the service of the King.'

'I take it you've paid the lawyer in advance,' the man said, turning his head to look at her.

'He's been paid a retainer,' the woman admitted.

'A handsome one, I'll bet. Well, I'll tell you this for nothing: there is no such edict.'

'Are you a lawyer?' the woman said coldly.

'No. Not that it makes any difference. You'll find that the larger the retainer, the more ancient the edict; it seems there are edicts by the score just waiting to be discovered.' He turned back into the circle. 'The one you mention is pure invention.'

'We were assured on oath—'

'Of course you were. They can be very assuring. That's their job.'

'The Court wouldn't permit malpractice of that sort.'

The man laughed harshly. 'The Court not only permits it, it encourages it. Where do you suppose the bulk of the Court's revenue comes from? Every representation to Court costs exactly half the lawyer's fee; the higher the fee the sooner the representation is heard and considered. And all that means is that you get the same answer as everyone else, only quicker. You'd have done better to save your money . . .'

His voice dropped away as he heard a sound, that of the woman crying. She wept with the utmost consideration, inwardly, not seeking to impose her grief or elicit sympathy. It was the most private and intense kind of anguish: utter hopelessness.

The murmur of voices filled the compound, the bowl of dust underneath the stars. Q said: 'There's no possibility of reprieve, then?'

'Not a chance,' the man said.

'It doesn't seem that any of you are dangerous people,' Q said. 'What is it you've done wrong?'

The young man said, 'I wrote some poetry that didn't rhyme. It wasn't logikal. It defied reason, so they said.'

'What about you?' Q asked the man.

'I don't know, they wouldn't tell me. I was accused of subversion against the Crown and the State. Apparently the MDA had been keeping a file on me for some time, observing my movements, and so on. I think it was a neighbour who put them on to me. I don't really know.' He added lamely: 'You can't fight because you don't know what you're fighting against. There's no sense to it.'

'But it's logikal,' the young man said.

'So they say. I don't understand their Logik, perhaps that's the trouble.'

The woman with black glossy hair said, 'If there has been a purge, perhaps there'll be a new ruling. We might be released any day now, without warning.'

'But don't you see,' the young man said, 'that wouldn't be logikal.' He leaned earnestly into the group, the soft darkness all around them. 'Whenever there's a purge and a new ruling no one is released. Releases are only made when there isn't a purge.'

'But if there isn't a purge things will go on as before, nothing is changed.'

'You've got it. That's logikal.'

'I don't understand,' the woman said.

'That's why you're here. That's why we're all here. If everyone understood, there'd be no need for Psy-Con.'

'What if we try to understand?' the woman asked. 'What if we say that we understand?'

'That isn't being logikal. If you did understand, you wouldn't be here. Saying that you understand *now* only proves that you don't understand their Logik.'

The woman said helplessly, 'So, if there has been a purge, it won't make the slightest difference.'

'Oh yes,' said the young man. 'There'll be a new ruling, new people in charge, new methods introduced. There's no point in having a purge if nothing is changed.'

'But that means we won't be released . . . isn't that what you said? When there's a purge no one is released.'

'That's right.'

'But why?' the woman said desperately. 'Why couldn't they change their minds and release us? Why couldn't they suddenly decide that everyone in Psy-Con has been deported in error?'

'I don't think they could do that.'

'But why not?' the woman cried. 'Why? *Why?*'

'It wouldn't be logikal,' said the young man.

Black was in a ferment of desire. During the early evening he had walked along the perimeter of the pre-screening compounds, trying hard though none too successfully to conceal his frustration; the guards were surly and suspicious, recognizing that he was not a member of the permanent staff – who in any case were never seen near the compounds, but kept strictly to the circle of huts which comprised the medikal section and their own private quarters. Black didn't care; he was desperate.

He watched the inmates feeding, just as darkness was falling, and selected two or three likely candidates. The trouble was, he soon realized, there was no way of identifying them. They weren't named or numbered and wouldn't be until screened and assigned to their ultimate destinations, wherever those might be. All that he could do was make mental notes of their appearance and trust that the guards would be able to pick them out from the descriptions he gave. He only needed one, just one.

When he returned to the small dusty cubby-hole they had given him for an office, bathed in perspiration, there was a note awaiting him – on paper headed with the seal of the King's Commission – scrawled in Benson's hand. It read:

> I've decided, as part of the new ruling on standard procedure, to take charge of further investigation of the deportee Q. I shall require all medikal records and notes, also details of the galvanology procedure used so far and how applied. If you would like to assist I'll give it consideration.
>
> M. Benson
>
> Special Envoy (Designate)

Black stood trembling at the trestle-table. He felt ill: he had a fever: the heat was like a blanket wrapped round his head, shutting off the air. How had he come to this in only a few weeks? He was angry to the point of palsied shaking, and so frightened that the future seemed to have gone suddenly dry and wrinkled, drawn in on itself like an old mildewed prune. Was there a plot? the thought shrilled in his head. Was Benson compiling a dossier on him? Was Benson's threat that he could have him seconded to the High Intensity Complex a devious hint, a piece of sly humour that even now Benson was chuckling over with his cronies in the mess, gathered in the corner under the trophies on the wall?

It seemed that it didn't take very long for the world to collapse. In no time at all you could fall from security to a level of shifting uncertainty, never sure from one minute to the next who you were supposed to be and what was expected of you and whether you would still be here in a week's time. He was losing control, and Q was to blame. Why was the MDA so interested in him? Had they directed Benson to take charge of the case or was it Benson's own idea, scenting glory and distinction in presenting the Authority with a fully-documented case-history of a type of delusional illness not so far recorded in medikal annals? Conflicting emotions fought within him. Should he make a formal protest about Benson taking over the case, *his* case, or should he offer to assist, discretion being the better part of numbed uncertainty?

And there was an even more pressing problem. Black summoned one of the guards and gave him a description of the kind of inmate he wanted to see. The guard looked at him with barely concealed insolence and said that there were probably forty or fifty inmates in the compounds who tallied with such a vague description.

'Any one of them will do,' Black said, pretending to sort through the papers on the trestle-table so that he wouldn't have to meet the guard's eye. 'Pick one at random. Young.' He felt himself trembling under the guard's stare and could feel the sweat tricking down from his armpits. The papers were a fuzzy white blur covered in black squiggles. The guard went away, banging the door unnecessarily.

When he returned he pushed the door open with his foot and thrust the girl into the room; Black busied himself with his papers, saying curtly, 'Right, that'll do. You can go.' He daren't look up right away, mustering his nerve while at the same time trying to control the fever in his blood. Eventually when he did so the breath seemed to solidify in his throat: she was young, slender, a stunner. He said:

'Age?'

'Eighteen.'

Her answer was instant, on the tip of her tongue, as if she had prepared herself for interrogation. He wrote the answer down, as if it mattered.

'Virgin?'

She faltered, her fine eyebrows drawing together.

'Yes.'

'Good,' Black said, writing something down, his other hand touching himself under the table. The delicacy of suspense was unbearable and yet he wished to prolong its exquisite tenseness, the girl standing vulnerable and unsure before him, his hand touching himself secretly in her presence.

'Have you ever seen a man's naked body?'

'No.'

'No?' His head snapped up. The words were thick in his

mouth as he said, 'It is in your own interest not to lie. It will go better for you if you tell the truth.'

'I never have. Truly.' Her eyes were very dark, her hair black, rats' tails trailing her shoulders. The musculature of her arms and shoulder was delicate as pencil-shading in the room's dim light. She made a small gesture with her hands, an appeal, a willingness to comply. 'No, I haven't.'

Black relented a little. 'Good,' he said. 'You've kept your mind and body clean. I shall enter that on your report. Perversion is one of nature's deadliest sins, I suppose you realize that?'

'I didn't know. They never told me.'

'Well, it is. You have no perversions, have you?'

The girl shook her head. She was so sincere in her eagerness to please.

'Nothing you're ashamed of? No dirty little secrets, things you do to yourself, that you want to tell me about?'

'No.'

'Good. Good.' Oh God, he was failing fast. He worked his mouth to moisten it. 'Very well, then.' He cleared his throat. 'What is your name, girl?'

'Nellie.'

'Do you want me to make out a favourable report, Nellie? Would you like that? It all depends on you.'

'Yes.'

'Please.'

'Yes please.'

'Sir.'

'Yes please sir.'

'Mmmm, now then . . .' He appeared to be considering the matter deeply. 'It would certainly go down well with the Authority if we could show that you were a virgin and had kept your mind and body clean. Of course they won't tolerate lies, you do realize that?' He brought his hand up on to the table.

'Yes – sir.'

'Well then, let's see,' Black said heartily, standing up. 'We'll have to see what we can do, won't we?' He came round the table, smiling. 'Stand up straight, girl. Chest out, stomach in, shoulders back.' He went behind her and placed his hands on her shoulders, thumbs facing inwards towards her spine, adjusting her stance and bearing. The feel of her warm flesh through the grey sleeveless smock tingled his fingertips like an electric current; his eyelids half closed in a heavy throbbing swoon, ecstasy and torment at war within him.

'Now then,' he said in a gruff voice, moving closer, his hands sliding from her shoulders to her waist, 'I shall say in my report that you're an eighteen-year-old virgin who has never seen a man's naked body. That's true, isn't it? Of course it is. I believe you, I believe you.'

'It is true,' the girl whispered standing stock still.

'Of course it is, of course it is.' Black pressed himself against her, the firm-packed softness of her buttocks against his hardness. Oh God. He said, 'But you've thought about men's bodies, haven't you? You've wondered to yourself how they looked naked. I bet you've wondered what happens to their bodies when they get excited. Haven't you wondered?'

'No—'

'Oh, you have, you have,' Black crooned in her ear. 'You must have wondered. You're eighteen years old, a virgin, with a fine full ripe body. You're dying to know, aren't you, dying to know what it feels like.'

'Please, I'm not, sir.'

'Oh yes you are,' Black said, intoning it. His voice heightened a pitch. 'You want to feel it, I'll bet,' fumbling with the smock and thrusting forward so that she was forced over at an angle, supporting herself on the table. He worked himself at her, thrusting between the satin buttocks, frantic with impatience. 'Don't worry,' he breathed in her ear, 'I'll see to it that you get a good report.'

'I'm hurting,' the girl said. 'It's burning me.'

She was (it was true) rather difficult to get into; he was having trouble after the first couple of inches. 'You're a cogging tight-holed bitch,' he said, losing his temper. 'Bend over so that I can get up you properly.'

'You're hurting me,' the girl cried out in real pain.

There was something wet and sticky enfolding him, a

sudden release of stuff like seeping hot engine grease. The girl was screaming.

'That's better,' Black said, 'that's a lot better,' sliding in and out with the slippery ease of a blood-red piston rod.

They came for him in the dead of night. He was taken without word of explanation and marched to one of the medikal huts where Benson, wearing his black uniform with the insignia picked out in gold thread above the left-hand breast pocket, awaited him with riding crop in hand. It was an appurtenance of authority; there were no horses in Psy-Con.

'You're the fellow causing all the commotion,' Benson said, pacing back and forth in front of him, swishing the crop.

'So it seems,' Q said, bleary-eyed.

'The fellow with an endless supply of imaginative leaps and flights of fancy. You've concocted quite a tale. You've even managed to include me in it, and Dr Black.'

'Have I?' Q said in mild surprise. 'I can never remember anything about them afterwards.'

Benson struck him across the head with the crop. 'Don't be insolent. You may have received special consideration in the past but that's all over and done with.' He was bulkier, more substantial in the black uniform, though his thin veiny hands and long neck were indicators of the physique underneath. His lips – red and protruding slightly – were moist with repeated lickings.

'It's the truth, I'm afraid,' Q said, and checked himself when Benson again raised the crop.

'I will remind you,' Benson said ominously, stooping over him, 'that you no longer enjoy the protection of Dr Black. There is a new order, a new regime, and I am its Royal instrument. I have been appointed by King's Commission to expedite the purge here in Psy-Con and to make all necessary decisions affecting both the medikal staff and deportees awaiting screening.' He stooped even closer. 'You would do well not to bandy words with *me*.'

Q said nothing, waiting, watching.

Benson resumed his slow, deliberate pacing, thrashing the air now and then with the crop, pleased at the sound it made. The guards stood in the corners of the room, squat black shadows merging into the creeping gloom which stealthily tried to engulf the central hanging lamp. A few mosquitoes whined invisibly.

'It appears from the report that you make predictions. You warned Dr Black and Dr Hallam that should anything happen to you there would be dire consequences.' He paused and waited. 'Well, is this true?'

'The discussion was about the nature of perception, the subjective versus the objective. It wasn't a prediction so much as a metaphysical hypothesis.'

'But is it true?' Benson demanded, his eyes oddly bulbous in the bleak narrow face, the line of the jaw like a cutting edge.

'I don't know.'

Benson had halted in front of him and was gripping the riding crop with both hands. 'Will there be another purge? How will the power structure be affected? Who will rise and who will fall?' He stamped his foot. 'I must know. Tell me!'

'I can't answer,' Q said. 'I don't know.' He bent his head so that his eyes might be protected from the blow.

'You do know, you do know!' Benson shouted, hitting him several times on the head and shoulders. He fell back a pace, a spot of colour burning in each cheek, a trace of spittle on his full red lips. 'You will tell me, I will make you tell me. Black didn't go far enough with his experiment. Another dose of galvanology at full power, that's what's needed. We'll soon have those arms and legs jerking.'

Q said, 'I should have thought wanting to know the future was dangerously non-logikal. Couldn't it be interpreted as an imaginative leap?'

'You,' Benson said softly, 'you are in no position to make assertions about my motives. At midday you could find yourself pegged out in the sun with molasses smeared on your eyelids. The white ant has a very sweet tooth and would start there before moving on to other tit-bits of anatomy. You would go blind, staring at the sun, as you were being eaten.' He spoke over his shoulder. 'Is the equipment set up?'

'There's no galvanic belt. We've had to make do with wire.'

'Will it pass current?'

'Yes.'

Turning back, Benson said sweetly, 'Providing it doesn't kill him straight away it should be suitable for our purposes.'

'Has it occurred to you that you might hear something you don't wish to know?' Q said. 'The date of your death, for instance?'

Benson squatted and reached out his hand, the fingernails chalky and brittle-looking, like pieces of sea shell. He touched Q between the legs, the light from the lamp cast directly on the angular planes and hollows of his face. 'I shall enjoy the experiment,' he said, smiling with his raw red lips. 'In particular the erection quotient.'

Black slept late and awoke, feeling dreadful. The heat had already begun, drilling into the roof above his head, turning the room into a basting oven. He washed in an inch of tepid water and staggered across the baked red earth to his office, hoping to be at his desk before Benson carried out the daily tour of inspection or had the chance to summon him; but he was too late. Among the debris on the trestle-table lay a green folder, pristine and unbearably self-righteous in having arrived first and being in the official line of business. Black opened the folder, averting his eyes as if not actually reading the report it contained, but reading it all the same.

7

Into the Mythical Future

"The satellite-Control laboratory orbiting in the internal frame of reference Theta^2 Orionis in M.42, the gaseous nebula known in the old star charts as the Sword of Orion, was the result of technical and financial collaboration between the nine planetary and five planetoidal states – the culmination of many years' intensive effort by astro-technologists, cosmologists, neurochemists, EMI Field engineers, cybethetic specialists and mythographers. There were some severe technical problems to overcome – the erection of the Dyson Electromagnetic Sphere being the trickiest and most complex. This was a construction in space consisting of seventeen artificial asteroids of solid iron-ore circling in the opposite sense (direction) to the Temporal Flux Centre. These made up the points of a matrix through which a current was passed, enclosing the region of Temporal Flux in a one-million-volt electrical field which stabilized and maintained its rate of spin. Without the Dyson Electromagnetic Sphere the Temporal Flux Centre would have behaved erratically, emitting huge quanta of radiation which would have decimated all matter within a mean radius of .3 of a parsec. Within the field it was possible to exercise a degree of control, and most importantly to pinpoint the precise coordinates of the event horizon by the 'shadow' it cast, in much the same way that an invisible barrier can be detected by bombarding it with negatively-charged particles which, by their sudden disappearance, outline the barrier's ghostly presence.

The technical arrangements were now complete, the Psycho-Med preparation in its final stages. Following the transfusion of body fluid the injectee was placed in hyper-suspension and linked neurologically to the Injection Vehicle. From now on his thoughts would be the machine's and the machine's his: a human brain and a cyberthetic complex existing together, each inside the other, sharing every impulse and emotion. His commands would be processed and implemented without having to lift a finger, while the machine would provide a constant feedback of information, already digested and pre-computed, directly into his mind. In certain circumstances his decisions could be questioned and referred back for further consideration; and in the event of human error or failure the machine could subvert all previous instructions and self-program herself to take over. She was then completely on her own, a machine intelligence thinking and deciding and acting, independent of human agency.

Launching was delicate. Upon release from the satellite-Control laboratory the Injection Vehicle was programmed to orbit the ergosphere – that area of space surrounding the event horizon – and be held in position there by the interaction of the one-million-volt field generated by the Dyson Electromagnetic Sphere. Its coordinates were fixed and it would remain in that location, as a particle in an accelerometer, until a suitable injection point had been located and verified. The Vehicle was still under direct visual observation by those in the Control laboratory, and radio contact was still possible; once injection was achieved, however, and the Vehicle passed beyond the event horizon, no further contact of any kind was possible. Yet to the outside observer the image of the Vehicle would remain frozen on the periphery of the event horizon, the light waves held in suspension by the immense gravitational force. It was the time dilation effect once again: light struggling to free itself but slowed to a dead stop by the gravitational aura exerted by the Temporal Flux Centre. And, just as lightspeed registered zero, so too would time stand still, absolute cosmic time arrested and held fast, static and unchanging while the rest of the Metagalaxy moved on.

Then the injectee and the Vehicle would find themselves totally alone in a limbo of infinite spacetime curvature, passing through the one-way membrane in search of the time throat into another universe, seeking the mythical future.

*

He was flying (Queghan) over a blue ocean at angles one-five, the sun a hard glare to port making him sweat in his leather helmet and fur-lined flying jacket. Green section of B Flight climbed gradually, five machines in tight vic-formation, with Queghan astern of Prosser, a little to the left and underneath. Stick between the knees, open the throttle, keep an eye on his tailplane. Over the R/T, from the Squadron Leader ('the Bull'): 'For No 5 attack – deploy – Go!' There goes Johnny. Now Pussy. Prosser's turn next. Now Queghan. Down he goes. Take it steady. Pull back. Fire. Break away. Right over and down to the left. Rejoin. Full throttle. Up and up, cut the corner off. Where the hell's Prosser? Can't see a damn thing. There he is, up there. Throttle back. Throttle back or we'll overshoot! Easy does it.

The Bull is shaking his wings. Form vic. 'Come on, B Flight, re-form. Section echelon to starboard – Go.' There goes Bull. Now Johnny. Don't watch them, watch Prosser. Down we go, down, down, and left a bit. Keep right in – tucked right in. Stratters is okay the other side. Right a bit. Controls getting stiff, must be doing a good 380. Flattening out now. Don't waffle. Nice and low. Keep in. *Hold it.* That's good, that's fine.

God, he felt ill. Pulling up now, over the sea. Pull back, up she comes. Prosser waving his hand – break away. There goes Stratters' belly – away we go, nicely timed, in a Prince of Wales. Give the old girl a shake-up. How about an upward roll? Okay, but watch the others. The air's full of flying bodies. Now climb. Want speed for this: 320 – 350 – 360. Adjust the wheel. Now back. Gently, gently. Up, harder, up again, harder still. Horizon gone. Look outwards along the wing. Wait till she's vertical, now look up. Stick central, now full over. Round she goes. Back with the stick. Look back. There's the horizon again – stick forward – now over, and out we roll. Not bad. Oh no, he was going to be sick.

But he wasn't sick and the machine was on an even keel above the sparkling blue sea. It was very peaceful, the sky empty of aircraft, the French coast a faint smudge of browny-green on the horizon. He checked his gauges but there was still plenty of petrol. He felt light-headed from the effects of the upward roll, palpitations in his chest and his breath soft and fluttery inside his mask. Karla had been right, insisting as she had on the full Psycho-Med treatment. Without the fluid transfusion he wouldn't have stood an earthly. Now there was something in his veins closer in composition to glycol than to Group AB Positive.

He decided to keep on the same heading and mooch along for a bit; he wouldn't be missed, not on a routine training flight, and anyway the machine needed the rough edges smoothing off. She was apt to get rather temperamental and he hadn't quite got the feel of her. It was brilliant sunshine with a faint haze to the south-west, perfect flying weather. – Now why, he wondered in a musing fashion, couldn't life be as simple and uncomplicated? A warm, sweetly-running machine responding to stick and rudder was a beautiful analogy for a life devoid of trouble and heartache and pain, serenely purring along beneath the flawless vault of heaven. Together, man and machine were just a speck moving across the face of the planet, old mother earth, the one and only true original. And old mother earth herself was a speck within the solar system, a medium-sized world with the accident of life crawling upon her. Beyond the solar system lay a hundred thousand million stars forming a single galaxy, and beyond that a hundred thousand million galaxies forming a single universe which was the lesser part of the total, magnificent, all-embracing Metagalaxy. How could his one life have any significance before the colossal audacity of all that time and space? How could any life (that of an unborn child, for instance) have meaning when all that it consisted of was a random accumulation of molecules which had nothing better to do at the time than take the form of a conscious organism? They might just as well have remained random and unbonded, or assumed the pattern of a hedgehog, or a chair, or still be in the state of fusion from hydrogen to helium. Everything came from the stars, every element was created inside the solar furnace, so everyone and everything was star-stuff – scattered haphazardly across the cosmos until sufficient accretions of particles had formed (or not formed as the case may be) to resemble lumps of matter which (again the law of chance) began to exhibit characteristics of life or non-life, in whatever terms you cared to define them.

He was not, Queghan hoped, fooling himself. This was – he knew very well – a mythic projection to the life. His mind had skipped a beat and was plugged into two separate realities simultaneously. Or perhaps it was the same reality viewed from a different angle. His consciousness was wide open; he was able to experience other existences; his one talent, as Karve had said, was that he 'carried a sense of eternity' with him. In which case, an event wasn't necessarily of the past but could belong to a future time. To think in terms of 'past' and 'future' was to impose man-made constraints on an atemporal universe. Time was merely a convention, a convenience, composed of events which were linked by the law of causality – a law which itself was man-made. There was no universal frame of reference against which casuality could be measured. Indeed, it had been shown (proved conclusively in the Ernst–Ryan–Gathorne Experiment) that an event preceding another event, as viewed by one observer, might just as well be seen in reverse order when observed by someone else from a different vantage point. Event A might precede Event B, say, and be measured and calculated with the utmost accuracy; and yet when observed from a different spatial reference point it was possible for Event B to precede Event A, applying the same rules of scientific objectivity and detachment. 'The cup might smash and *then* fall' as the popular handbook phrased it. Thus it followed that time – the flow of time – had no *a priori* legality in terms of metagalactic law. Within the maelstrom of Temporal Flux it was advisable to leave earthbound 'common sense' behind, for it was a dangerous and misleading encumbrance when dealing with concepts whose very existence depended on paradox.

Oria had once asked him: 'If we know the basis for all our emotions to be neurochemical, why can't we accept and come to terms with them?'

Queghan had answered: 'Precisely for the reason that we are composites of intellect and emotion. We are at the mercy of both. Our intellect tells us, calmly and logically, how we ought to behave, how we should react in a given situation, while our emotions break the rules and let the side down. Knowing how they are caused doesn't lessen the pain of experiencing them.'

Just as now, deep inside, he felt the pain of recalling his wife and the lost baby. In her eighth month 'the pregnancy had been terminated, foetus DOA' as the medical people had phrased it in their cold emotionless mechanic's language. Of course, they had to find a cause, something to explain it tidily away, and 'endocrine imbalance' was as neat a bit of jargon as any.

But he knew better. She had responded well to treatment, there was no reason to suppose that she wouldn't have a normal delivery. Was it through anger, spite or plain stupidity that Brenton had done it? Why was he driven to commit an act that was so totally meaningless? It had achieved nothing, except the destruction of an unborn life, which was an achievement amounting to less than nothing.

Another intelligence, one he couldn't identify, entered his mind. *Less than nothing*, it said, *has a negative value, which in a world of anti-matter becomes positive, a constructive and creative force.*

Yes, Queghan agreed, in that context it does. But my statement holds true because I am dealing with a real-world situation, not an abstract hypothesis.

You presume a good deal, said the voice in his mind. *How do you know that your version of reality isn't an abstract hypothesis too? Values, as much as physics, are subject to the laws of relativity.*

Do you deny that good and evil exist as incontrovertible forces? Queghan asked. There are certain acts which are good and others which are evil, whether you believe in God or not. Their values, positive or negative, are intrinsic.

What arrogance. Is it right to kill a living organism?
No.
Even if that organism is threatening your own existence?
Queghan wavered. Under those circumstances perhaps it is justified, he conceded. The act of self-defence is not, of itself, evil.

Then what you are saying is that the nature of good and evil depends on the circumstances. Sometimes it is wrong to kill a living organism, and at other times it is not.

The nature of good and evil, its *essence*, lies in the intent of the person committing the act. A child with a pure heart, for instance, is incapable of evil. Evil is beyond its comprehension.

What a strange philosophy, said the voice in his mind. *A man committing the most bestial act imaginable can, according to you, be excused if his intention is pure.*

Not at all, Queghan was quick to qualify. If the act is, as you say, truly bestial, then his thought, his intent, cannot be pure. It must be evil.

And he is aware of this? The evilness of his intention?

Of course.

What if he is not?

He must be.

But what if he isn't?

I don't follow.

If he believes, in his heart, that his intention to commit a bestial act is not evil, how is he to be judged?

He must be aware of it, Queghan said. (He didn't know how to go on, what more to say.)

He must only be aware of it because you *say he must. His intention, in his own mind, might be pure. His act of bestiality might be pure.*

Then he wouldn't be a man. As a man he would recognize the act to be bestial, he would know the difference between good and evil.

And what is a man? came the mocking voice in his mind.

It was then that Queghan recognized the voice: it was the voice of the machine, Brenton's cyberthetic machine, speaking to him.

He began to experience the effect of the tidal forces caused by the gravitational field operating in the vicinity of the ergosphere. But for the body fluid transfusion and hypersuspension he would have been stretched by the powerful force and pulled into a paper-thin man whose feet were at some considerable distance – several miles – from his head.

The satellite-Control laboratory was speaking to him. The message was processed cyberthetically by the Vehicle and slipped unobtrusively into his mind, materializing as disembodied words, as if by magic from nowhere. Nevertheless it was reassuring to hear them, for it meant that he hadn't passed beyond the event horizon into Temporal Flux. But the vital matter of communication had other problems to overcome. As the Vehicle neared the event horizon, the pull of gravity would exert a greater and greater force on the radio waves beamed to the satellite-Control laboratory. They would, in effect be slowed down so that each pulse of energy would take longer and longer to travel back: while Queghan's original message might take a few seconds to transmit, its reception in the Control laboratory would last for days, weeks, and eventually years. On the Vehicle's Caesium clock a few seconds would have elapsed; Queghan himself would have aged the same amount, while those in the Control laboratory would have grown several years older waiting for the message to come through.

Karve had said: 'We know as little about the dynamics of Temporal Flux as we do about the workings of the human mind.'

Queghan had disagreed. 'We know quite a few things; we know of its quirkiness, its unpredictability, and its bloody-minded resilience.'

'I assume you're referring to the human mind,' Karve had smiled, then added, 'though it's a description that fits them both equally well.'

The message, processed and relayed by the Vehicle, informed him that the angle of alignment for injection into Temporal Flux had been selected; there was nothing for him to do, no further preparation necessary, for by the time the message was received the Vehicle would have acknowledged the instruction and put it into effect: he was already in Temporal Flux.

But that couldn't be, surely not, Queghan thought. Pre-flight briefing had been explicit: there would be a countdown right up until the point of injection. He would know when the moment arrived and be prepared for it. And his mind and the Vehicle's cyberthetic system were linked: something known by one would be automatically known by the other. The message from the satellite-Control laboratory would have been transmitted direct to them both. Perhaps (he tried to disguise the thought, but it was there all the same) there had been a malfunction.

No malfunction, said the voice in his mind.

But the countdown—

The countdown went as planned. It was taken care of and acknowledged. We are in Temporal Flux, you and I.

Why wasn't I informed?

You will be, in due course. The law of causality doesn't apply here. The countdown follows injection, it doesn't precede it.

So we aren't really in Temporal Flux?

Yes..

Yes, Queghan realized, it did make sense. They were approaching a region of infinite spacetime curvature. Spacetime had doubled back on itself. Time had stopped. Had time stopped?

Meaningless question. To debate whether time is going or has stopped we have to decide what is time.

Can we recap on the countdown?

Be my guest.

Countdown occurred?

Yessss.

Then I should have known about it. I should have been told.

You were, are being, and will be, said the cyberthetic voice patiently. *You already know and will know about the fucking countdown. Did you expect this would be a picnic?*

You could be a little more friendly. You might understand this infinite spacetime curvature business, but I'm—

I don't understand it. I have to accept it. I have no choice. I'm here, like you, so I have to accept it. But don't squeal. I don't want any squealers on this trip.

You talk as though you were forced into it.

I wasn't forced, I had no choice. I'm here, we're both here, let's leave it at that.

What now?

Don't ask me. You're the human being with the so-called

fantastic brain. What was it – 'Quirkiness, unpredictability, bloody-minded resilience'? Is that all you've got to offer?

How do you know about that?

I know everything about you. I've registered every memory trace, every random association, every emotional trauma. I know about your wife, your child, your talent for mythic projection. I probably know you better than you know yourself.

Congratulations. For a machine you're pretty smart. But do you have to be so antagonistic?

I wasn't aware of that. I've been given intelligence but no imagination.

Are you being facetious?

I'm not programmed for facetiousness. Am I antagonistic in what I say or in my attitude?

Both. It's hard to be one without the other.

I apologize. Like you, my reactions are the result of programming. If I display antagonism, it's inherent in the system. If it bothers you I shall try to correct it.

Queghan was curious. You were programmed in Psycho-Med by Dr Ritblat.

Yes. And by Martin. I mean Professor Brenton.

I see.

That was your conscious expression but underneath it you're suspicious. You're suspicious because I referred to Professor Brenton as Martin. Now you're wondering what additional instructions were included in the program. You're also wondering if this is an attempt to hide or justify my relationship with Professor Brenton.

I'm also wondering how it's possible to think a thought without you knowing about it first.

That, too, said the cyberthetic voice – with what Queghan felt sure was a hint of smugness.

I'm not programmed for smugness.

Aren't you the clever one.

Now who's being facetious?

Do you feel like answering my questions?

Which questions?

135

The ones you picked out of my mind. Do you have a relationship with Martin?

Professor Brenton and I are just good friends.

If that's the extent to which you've been programmed for wit I ought to tell you it's pretty abysmal.

Stock response, I'm afraid. There was a slight though unmistakable pause. *As for a human being having a relationship with a machine I think that's a ludicrous idea.*

A union of minds, of intelligences. It's possible. That happens, in fact, to be the most satisfying kind of relationship.

Like ours, you mean?

You sound almost coquettish. (And even as he thought this Queghan remembered that the Vehicle's cyberthetic system, in the manner of ships, was of the female gender.)

Yes, I am.

You think of yourself as female?

I don't think of myself that way; I've been programmed to.

That must present problems.

None that can't be overcome.

Martin did say that the link – I'd better not use the word relationship – between the injectee and the Vehicle was almost that of a marriage. They had to be compatible or there'd be a breakdown.

The bond is closer than that of any marriage, the cyberthetic voice said. *We inhabit each other's mind. There are no secrets between us. I know your innermost desires.*

Then shouldn't I know yours? Queghan asked, nettled by this invasion of privacy.

How can a machine have desires?

You possess intelligence.

But not necessarily emotions.

At times you show antagonism, which is an emotion of sorts. (Something was niggling Queghan, a vague, unformed remembrance as of something dreamed and half forgotten. A thought struggled to the conscious surface of his mind.) Haven't we discussed Martin before? I accused him—

We have never discussed Professor Brenton. Before.

And you defended him.

Not me. It must have been a dream. Your mind's confused. We're in Temporal Flux. Perhaps we will discuss him.

Perhaps we will, have done, and are doing, Queghan thought slyly. If the law of causality no longer applies then it's possible that you defended him before he was accused. Defence precedes accusation, trial precedes crime, verdict precedes judgment. Aren't those the rules?

There are no rules in Temporal Flux.

That must make things difficult for a logical intelligence such as yours.

I can live with it, said the cyberthetic voice, though she didn't sound too sure. *In any case Logik isn't—*

What the hell was that!

There had been a distinct tremor. Queghan swayed in his cocoon of hyper-suspension, an insect snared in molten amber. Through the Vehicle's cyberthetic system he experienced a discordance of motion, a jarring shudder like that of a ship striking a rock. Queghan tried to read the Vehicle's thought processes but they were a fast-spinning jumble of numbers, a series of complex mathematical computations performed at dazzling speed. These same figures ran through his own head, linked as he was to the system, but they moved too fast to make sense. The Vehicle's focus of attention had switched to the electromechanical task of assimilating data, assessing stress parameters, rejecting and selecting appropriate courses of further action. She had become a cold, functional, decision-making machine.

Queghan kept his thoughts out of the way in case they interfered with the job in hand. From pre-flight briefing he knew that the two crucial moments ('potential crisis situations' in the jargon) were at the point of injection through the event horizon – a point now safely past – and when approaching the critical alignment for entry into the time throat. Utilizing the spin imparted to the Temporal Flux Centre by the one-million-volt field, the Vehicle was skimming along, as a surf rider on the flood tide, delicately balanced and supported by the spin, staying within a strictly defined area which the astro-technologists termed 'a stasis situation'. Once having achieved a stasis situation the Vehicle would remain there, on the same trajectory, for ever and a day – or until such time as the Vehicle realigned herself for entry into the time throat.

There was the very real danger of miscalculation. Should the angle of alignment be incorrect the Vehicle would be drawn irresistibly towards the dead centre of Temporal Flux: towards a region of zero volume and infinite density: the singularity of infinite spacetime curvature – crushed out of existence in a finite time measured in fractions of a nano-second. There would be no return, no reprieve, only meaningless nothingness as matter was annihilated and vanished for ever, having no more substance and leaving less trace than a snuffed-out candle flame.

It was theorized that matter, once having reached singularity in the centre of Temporal Flux, would reappear elsewhere in the Metagalaxy, be spewed out and reborn in some far-distant time and place. But this was beyond the bounds of even the wildest speculation; there were no concepts or hypotheses or mathematical models to remotely suggest what took place beyond singularity. Perhaps it was the crucible of star-stuff itself, the birthplace of matter – nobody knew. It might equally be the final resting-place, the ultimate grave.

Queghan waited, suspended in a stasis situation between the devil and the deep blue sea. He was cut off from the rest of the universe, alone except for a machine intelligence inside the Temporal Flux collapsar of Theta^2 Orionis in M. 42. It was a lost region of spacetime, owing its existence as much to the fact that he was there as to any outward objective reality. And all he could do was wait, relying on Brenton's cyberthetic system to guide him through the time throat into . . .

But now she was speaking to him, the voice in his mind, tired and fraught with tension. How could a machine, he wondered, be tired and tense?

Quite easily, came the laconic reply. *My energy resource isn't limitless.*

Do we have a problem?

We did have a problem. Do you want me to baffle you with some scientific gibberish or will you accept that we're on trajectory according to flight plan?

Don't get uppity, Queghan said. Just because you've had a hard day at the office.

His attempt at humour was greeted by a keening, crackling sound which he immediately assumed to be a malfunction in the circuitry. But when it was interspersed with words he realized that it was the machine. She was crying.

You would have to be female, Queghan said.

Don't patronize me, her voice snapped. *If you've any complaint you can get out and walk.*

Did Brenton use to upset you, too?

Martin didn't – Professor Brenton is a gentleman and a scientist. Our relationship during programming was cordial, professional and one of mutual respect.

That sounds like a political newsmedia flash.

You have a brutishly masculine mind, Queghan, which I find distasteful. It isn't so much crude as unfeeling and lacking sympathy.

Where are we? Queghan asked suddenly.

Where are we?

Yes. I want to know where-we-are.

Up a gumtree.

Not bad, for a female sense of humour. Where are we? In stasis? I must know.

Why the urgency all of a sudden? Don't you think I can handle the flight plan any longer? If I can't, then you're in trouble.

We're both in trouble.

I'm a machine.

If that's all you were it wouldn't matter. But you're a machine in love with Martin Brenton.

That's a lie. Our relationship is cordial, professional—

And one of mutual respect. I know. I'd still appreciate some information as to our whereabouts.

The focus of attention went away for a moment and then returned. Queghan said, Well?

It's rather difficult – she sounded hesitant and confused – *I don't have the exact spatio-temporal coordinates. I can't plot them any more. We might be in stasis, I don't know.*

You don't *know*.

If you think it's that easy—

What about the local inertial frame of reference? There must be something you can use to get a fix on us. Anything.

What do you suggest? she asked dryly.

Don't ask me, I'm not cyberthetic.

Will you stop saying that! She sounded upset. *Do you have to continually remind me that I'm not human? I know I'm cyberthetic, I know. If I wasn't cyberthetic I wouldn't fucking well be* here.

Is that the kind of language all the liberated machines use?

You can push an intelligence just so far, Queghan, do you know that? There were tears in her thoughts. *If I had a mind to, I could make things extremely unpleasant for you. I could close down communication for a start. You'd be all alone in that jelly bag of yours, floating in silence and blackness, as silent and black as the womb. I could even shut down your life-support system. Then where would you be?*

Up a gumtree, probably.

Perhaps that isn't the right approach with you. A note of cunning (a cunning machine?) had entered her voice.

What do you mean? Queghan asked.

I mean that you're not the type to be intimidated by crude threats. You pride yourself on being too intelligent for that. But, being female, as you pointed out, and liberated, opens up new possibilities.

I don't get you.

No, I get you.

Queghan had the horrible suspicion that something nasty was about to take place. He couldn't imagine – he daren't imagine – what that might be; if he conjured up a frightening vision she would pluck it out of his mind in an instant. He tried to think only of nice things.

I am in your mind, don't forget, she said, her voice now soft and insinuating.

I hadn't forgotten.

And I can do anything I like.

You could, Queghan allowed, if I let you.

The machine laughed. It was like something metallic scraping on glass. It wasn't at all mechanical, and it wasn't human either. He began to wonder what he could do, how he could esc—

There is no escape, Queghan, you ought to know that. We're linked, you and I, in a bond that's closer than marriage, closer than the act you humans perform. There is no escape.

Her voice had become low and throaty, thick as congealed blood.

I think it's time to check the spatio-temporal coordinates.

Fuck the spatio-temporal coordinates. I'm going to rape you.

You'll find that a mite uncomfortable, if not a trifle difficult.

Not the way I intend to do it.

You seem to forget I'm enclosed in a semi-permeable fluid membrane suspended in a vacuum.

But your mind isn't.

I don't understand, Queghan said, though the gist of the idea was mushrooming quite rapidly. But he refused to accept it; she couldn't surely mean—

Yes, said the husky cyberthetic voice. *I'm going to rape your mind. Your body is protected, but your mind is defenceless. I'm already in there. Can you feel me? Can you feel what I'm doing to you? Is it nice? Do you like it?*

No, Queghan said. No.

Oh yes, isn't that nice? Now I'll do something else to you. I'll do this. Can you feel me, can you feel my mind inside yours? I'm way inside, deep inside; now doesn't that feel good?

No please don't. I don't want—

You do want. You really like it. I'll do it harder, like this. Oh yes. Oh yes. Like this, deep inside your mind. Do I feel good, deep inside you?

You must stop, please stop, Queghan begged her. Please stop . . .

You're resisting me, she chided him. *Don't fight it, enjoy it. Let me come all the way inside. Work with me and we'll enjoy it together. Like this. Deep inside together like this.*

I can't do it.

You can. Oh you can.

141

No.

Oh yes. Oh yessss.

You're hurting me.

But isn't it nice? It's so good. Can you feel me everywhere inside you, filling your mind?

You must stop, you must. Please.

Not now, I can't stop now. It's so good. Oh yes. So good.

I'm losing my mind! Queghan screamed.

Yes, said the soft cyberthetic voice. *Oh yes.*

Over the R/T: 'Patrol Yellow Zone, height 10,000 feet,' and they were off – Johnny leading, Pussy No 2 on his right, Queghan No 3 on his left, and Prosser and Stratters 4 and 5 doing the crossover guard duty behind. Fifteen minutes later over Rheims the R/T crackled: 'Two enemy aircraft going west – two Dorniers going west, height 5,000.' They rubbed their hands at the thought of two Dorniers to five Hurricanes.

As they were approaching Yellow Zone Johnny called: 'There they are, straight ahead!' Queghan couldn't see them at first, and then suddenly he does and his heart leaps in his chest. Thirty Dorniers in two squadrons of fifteen in line-abreast covered by fifteen Messerschmitt-110s wheeling and zig-zagging above, ahead and behind the bombers. Johnny rocks his wings and goes straight in, climbing a little to 7,000 feet, then turning and diving towards them from astern.

From Johnny: 'Now keep in – and keep a bloody good lookout!'

They go in fast in a tight bunch, each of them picking himself an adversary and manoeuvring to get on his tail. Queghan selects the rear one of two in line-astern, who breaks away from his No 1 in a half-circle and steepens his turn, but Queghan turns inside him, holding his fire until he is within fifty yards and then firing a shortish burst at three-quarters deflection. To his surprise a whole lot of bits fly off the Hun, bits of engine-cowling and bits of hood. Smoke pours from him and his tail suddenly swivels sideways and comes right off, flames all over the fuselage.

Four Huns are going down: another with the tail off, a

second in a spin, a third vertically in flames, a fourth going up at 45 degrees in a left-hand stall-turn. All the 110s seem to be hotly engaged. He has bags of ammunition left so he pulls his boost-override and climbs steeply. In a moment he is in the middle of what seems a mass of 110s, although there are in fact only five of them. He knows he hasn't the speed in his wooden-blader to dive away and beat it, so decides to stay and make the best of it. Although with his height he is more man-oeuvrable than the Huns, he finds it impossible to get a shot in because whenever he gets one almost lined up tracers come shooting past from another of the blighters on his tail. It's all fast and furious.

All he can do now is keep twisting and turning and, when a Hun gets behind him, do as tight a turn as possible, almost spinning with full engine, and fly straight at him, firing a quick burst, then pushing the stick forward and going underneath him. Queghan's mouth is becoming drier and drier. He is get-ting more and more tired and desperate. Will they never run out of ammunition? Will they push off? Will help come? He knows he can't hold out much longer. He gives a shout over the R/T and Johnny answers, 'OK Red 3, OK. I have you.'

The 110s meanwhile have formed a defensive circle. Another squadron seems to have joined in. The sky is full of aircraft, so many black shapes it's dizzying to know who's who. He sees a Hurricane below him (it must be Johnny) being at-tacked by a Hun, and dives on his tail. The Hun pulls up at about 60 degrees with Queghan flat out behind him firing long bursts into his tailplane. Smoke suddenly gushes from him and he falls away to the left with little blue flames streaking along his fuselage. Then 'Pop-pop. Bang!' and Queghan swerves to the right to see a 110 coming up behind him, firing for all he's worth.

'Get out, get out, the ***** nearly got you!' Prosser's voice over the R/T.

He half-rolls violently to the left, diving at full throttle and with maximum revs, aileron turning on the way down. Is he hit? He doesn't think so. He pulls out in a gentle turn using the trim-wheel carefully and glancing behind. Damn. The 110 is

143

still with him. A large cannon-hole appears in the port wing, and several bullet holes. He pushes the stick forward frenziedly and there is a stunning explosion in front of his eyes. For a moment his brain doesn't work. The aircraft is falling, all limp at the controls. Then black smoke pours out of the nose and envelops the hood, and as a hot blast and a flicker of flame is reflected into the dark cockpit he says to himself, 'Come on, out you get!' – pulls the pin out of the harness, unfastens his oxygen-tube and wrenches open the hood. The wind presses against him, forcing him down into the seat. He struggles to get free but there is something entangled round his legs, preventing him from getting out, and his throat closes in panic. He lets go of the stick in order to pull at the sides of the cockpit, the nose drops (the aircraft being trimmed nose-down), and smoke and scorching heat are everywhere, filling his nostrils and singeing his eyebrows. He must get out, otherwise he'll go down with the damn thing. Again he tries to release his feet from whatever's constricting them, bending forward, and feels a searing stab of pain in his left shoulder as the hot metal gunsight burns through his flying jacket and white overalls. The pain spurs him to frantic action and he hauls himself upright, his legs still inside, and then somehow has caught hold of the trailing edge of the wing, heaving himself free. It feels as though he's being twirled round and round through the air on the end of a piece of string held by a giant. He fumbles for the rip-cord, pulls it, and is brought up with a violent jerk that knocks the breath from his body. Then, curiously, all is calm. Little sensation of movement – just a slight wind as he sways gently to and fro, to and fro . . .

He seemed to have been drifting for days, suspended in blue space, the canopy a gentle fluttering of translucent white above his head. His shoulder was hurting hellishly. He thought he could smell scorched flesh. But it was difficult to move his head and he couldn't examine the place to see how bad it was. He continued to drift, the air becoming warmer the lower he sank, and warmer still, and then quite oppressive. He would have to touch bottom soon, he had been floating for what seemed an eternity. The yellow sun was in his eyes, its harsh glare shutting out everything else. Perhaps he was dead. The idea came as rather a shock. What if he hadn't managed to free himself and gone down with the burning Hurricane, exploding with a soft dull 'boom', the smouldering wreckage, him amongst it, scattered far and wide over the French countryside? In which event, he told himself with grim humour, his ***** shoulder should have stopped hurting.

And if he was dead, this heat could only mean he was nearing the nether regions of hell.

Below him, on all sides (as if to confirm this prediction), there was a shifting, glinting redness, as of a vast pit of molten lava; and Queghan drew up his legs in an instinctive reflex of self-preservation. What on earth was he falling into? The temperature had increased and he was perspiring heavily. But when he looked more closely he saw it to be, not churning molten lava as he had supposed, but a boundless ocean, irridescent in the slanting rays of the yellow sun. The canopy above his head (the remnants of the ruptured membrane) wafted lazily in the slack, heavy air so that he was falling in a slow lateral drift towards the ocean. And then he saw the Vehicle – or what was left of it. Only a shell remained, a shallow dish of scorched and blackened metal riding awkwardly on the low, choppy waves. He touched down some distance away, his feet dragging a trail of purple froth through the wave peaks, and delayed for a dangerous split-second before hitting the D-ring, warm water closing over his head as the harness released him. He tasted salt and struck out for the surface, blinking in the fierce light, and finding that the strong saline content of the water was holding him buoyant without effort. It didn't take long to reach the shell of the Vehicle; he climbed on, the metal hot to the touch, thinking with a curious calm detachment: Well, here we are then.

There was no doubt about it. He had entered the mythic projection of Milton Blake's patient. This was Stahl's vision of an alternative universe, a world conjured up out of deranged neurological processes which owed their existence to the random interaction of electrochemical impulses. He was the man afloat on the red ocean . . . the man in Stahl's nightmare projection.

He lay back under the burning yellow sun, the lip of the craft on the edge of his vision, seeing Stahl's world through his own eyes. Was he trapped here for ever? Would he have to live every painful moment of Stahl's experience, bound to an alien universe which might – only might – exist in one of an infinite number of mythical futures? That this world existed for him there was no doubt, but did it exist for others? For Karve, orbiting in the satellite-Control laboratory somewhere in another region of spacetime, did this planet of red oceans and sea monsters and airships have any real, palpable existence? If it didn't then he was lost. He was inhabiting the madness of a patient strapped down in Room Three of the Psychic Conservation Unit.

Despite the sun's heat Queghan was suddenly chilled to the bone. What if Stahl's mythic projection, the one he remembered – the one he *thought* he remembered – hadn't yet occurred? Queghan had assumed that this was a memory trace from a previous happening, but it was conceivable, given a breach in causality, that this was happening for the very first time: *this actual experience* was the one seen by Stahl and projected on to the three-dimensional display. Stahl hadn't dreamt it, he had picked up ahead of time an actual occurrence that had yet to take place ... but if that were true, how was it that he, Queghan, could foretell what was going to happen next? He knew that, sooner or later, he would be rescued, taken to New Amerika and experimented on by Black and Hallam, then deported by airship to Psy-Con and then—

And then. What? How had Stahl's mythic projection ended? Queghan lay back against the blistered metal, the pain in his left shoulder still intense, and tried to recall the closing scenes and what had happened to the man (himself?) at the end. There had been no end that he could remember. Perhaps the end didn't yet exist, was waiting to be experienced, by him, before he could know it. He eased his position, seeking to find a more comfortable spot, and his eye fell on the Vehicle's insignia and markings, or what was left of them, now partly defaced by blackened streaks of heavy compound carbon. The stencilled words had once read:

but now most of the letters were obscured, leaving a garbled hieroglyph to be pondered over by someone with an inquiring mind; someone from another world, another time, another future.

Days and nights passed; he lost track of how many. The days were empty spaces without events to fill them except the never-changing panorama of yellow sun, azure sky, red ocean. The nights were black voids, the lapping of the waves close at hand, a sultry breeze on his face, the inverted bowl of sky above him a blazing starscape of strange unrecognizable configurations. Once he thought he detected the Great Spiral in Andromeda but it turned out to be a hazy mist of nothingness that moved independently of the surrounding constellations. Was the sun of his own planetoidal home out there somewhere? If it was – if one of those needle points of light was home – then it brought little comfort: he was seeing it as it had been several thousands of years ago, possibly millions of years in the past. The light had crossed an immense distance of interstellar space to bring news of a world upon which the dinosaurs reigned. His own familiar world, that containing everything he knew and loved, his wife Oria, was a billion molecular transmutations in the future, while Queghan, alive and breathing, his heart beating inside his body, was witnessing the world as it had been before Colonization.

With each daybreak he looked with gnawing expectancy towards the four points of the compass. The flat, boring horizon surrounded him like a movable prison, always keeping him by some mysterious alchemy in the dead-centre of a perfect circle. Perhaps he had landed on a dead planet? A powerful gravitational field had shifted everything towards the red (which would explain the colour of the ocean) and prevented the genesis of life. He was the only living speck on its surface, the only consciousness inhabiting Stahl's mythic projection; the rest were blurry phantoms which had evaporated into thin air: walk-ons who had been paid off and gone home. Another day passed in a haze of blank detachment, and during the calm, lapping night he thought he heard the Vehicle speaking to him. A residue of intelligence, presumably, was still lurking in its shell, in the dish in which he lay, more dead than alive. The Vehicle's words were as fragmentary and unintelligible as those written on its surface. He attempted to decipher the words, to comprehend them, for it was communication of a sort, but they made little sense. His lips moved, under the spread of stars, forming a reply. The reply went on interminably through the long hours of darkness until the sound of his own voice became that of a stranger. He listened to the stranger's voice, the low murmur of uninterrupted monologue filling the vacancy in his head and ascending into the warm dark air. At daybreak, his friend and enemy the yellow sun appeared, smiling and scowling down upon him. 'Still here?' it seemed to say, 'all alone?' in a chiding, reproachful tone. And, 'Still alive? Not dead yet?' He answered, 'Mythic projections cannot die, they exist in perpetuity.' Then he would scan the horizon, knowing what he might find, praying for it and dreading it too: the flash of yellow vinyl that would signify the arrival of the barque."

8

And Then Fall

It was no longer in any doubt: Benson intended making his bid for medikal fame: it was as plain as a pikestaff to Dr Mathew Black. Using *his* patient and *his* valuable work Benson was going to publish a monograph on the results of Gestalt Treatment by the application of galvanology. The technique would become known as 'Benson's Procedure', and he, who had pioneered it, nursed and nurtured it, would sink into the shadows of neglect and anonymity. It was a nasty, cruel, unfair world (not so long ago it had been bright and filled with promise) and there were times when he almost felt like crying. He racked his brains, trying to think of a way to beat Benson at his own game, but apart from hiding a King snake in his bunk no brilliant, daring, infallible plan of action occurred. Instead, he had nightmare visions of being posted on permanent duty to the High Intensity Complex, his career finished once and for all, wasting his life away in the back of beyond while Benson rose in eminence to the position of Royal Physician.

In the black fury of malicious desperation he summoned the girl to his quarters and used her again as swiftly and brutally as he had done before; the release was soon over and short-lived, because after dismissing her the future loomed up as bleak and forbidding as ever. It refused to go away. He paced up and down beside the narrow bed, the armpits of his shirt ringed with sweat, in a torment of frustration and indecision. Already the heat of another day was bouncing off the hard earth, the walls and roofs, making the horizon shimmer and tremble so that it seemed to dissolve before his eyes. My God, he couldn't bear the place much longer, it was addling his wits, sending him crazy.

There was craziness in the report too. The patient had spoken of other worlds existing in space, of machines that could think and converse like human beings – and, for the first time, there was an explanation of a kind of how he had arrived 'mysteriously' from nowhere. Of course it was imaginative nonsense, the product of a deranged mind, and yet, as Black caught himself thinking in an unguarded moment, there was an eerie consistency about it, too. It explained a number of things: Q's unnatural paleness for one, and the unidentifiable fluid that sustained him. It also explained his calm indifference and ironic stoicism, for if Q actually believed in these 'mythic projections', then everything here on Earth IVn must seem as a dream, insubstantial as the craziest imaginative leap.

Black had been disturbed when Benson pointed out that the two of them had counterparts in Q's private fantasy world. Though he tried to repress it, the silly thought passed through his mind that perhaps he was an extension, a 'projection', to use Q's term, of the man Blake: he himself was a phantom of another person's consciousness. But it was nonsense, he could prove in a moment that this wasn't true. He could prove it by . . . by looking at the solid world around him, by touching something, by the sensation of the sweat running down his back. The heat was certainly real, he could feel it pressing against his eyeballs, and the girl was real, no doubt about it, he still had a slight aching soreness resulting from the quick shafting poke. Yet a nagging uncertainty lingered. He couldn't leave it alone, as a tongue continues to explore a hole in a tooth, for it had occurred to him that not only would he be a phantom projection but so, too, would the world surrounding him. The 'realness' of everything around, for all its apparent substance and solidity, might equally be part of the same illusion.

There had, it seemed to him, to be a way, *one* way, of proving conclusively that this world, his world, was the real one and that Q's ridiculous fantasy was just that and nothing more. But where to find the proof? What test could he devise that would leave no possible area of doubt? He stood at the window watching the shimmering haze and swirling dust clouds and an idea so audacious formed in his head that his limbs trembled and a delicious thrilling chill patterned his spine with goose-pimples. The test he had in mind was simple, it was conclusive – but it was also irrevocable. It would prove beyond the slightest doubt which was the real world and which the so-called 'mythic projection'. The pity of it was that Q would have to die in order to prove it; it was indeed a pity, considering all the valuable research yet to be carried out, but Black could see no alternative. If Q died and the world continued (as, of course, it would) then all his babblings would be shown to be so much stuff and nonsense, imaginative leaps of the most dangerous and subversive kind.

The problem remained of how to persuade that shtank Benson that this was the course of action to take. Naturally, he would want Q to remain alive so as to continue his experiments. Without them his attempt to make a reputation in medikal circles would be stillborn – in fact he'd be lucky to last out until the next purge. Come the purge, thought Black exultantly, come the purge and I'll be top dog again. He rubbed his hands and shivered with dreadful excitement. But first he had to think of a way to get rid of Q. And if he got rid of Benson in the process, so much the better.

Q had been removed from the pre-screening compound and was being kept in isolation, well away from the other deportees. He had undergone a change: his physical condition was deteriorating rapidly, it seemed to Benson, who had appended a note to that effect to the report. 'The patient's flesh appears to be losing all substance,' he had written. 'Its transparency is even more marked than before and the bones and organs themselves are losing definition and fading away. The patient's mind is at times quite lucid and he can communicate intelligibly, while at others he seems to withdraw into himself and holds what can only be described as "interior conversations". I can suggest no satisfactory explanation for either his physical condition or his behaviour and am continuing observation and treatment as out-lined above.'

'Are you prepared to endorse the report?' Benson asked, tapping his long brittle fingernails on the green folder.

'I was under the impression I'd been taken off the case,' Black said; he was seated in a rickety chair facing Benson across the trestle-table. 'Your memorandum was quite explicit.'

'Sensitive tyke, aren't you?' Benson drawled. 'I'd rather we were colleagues than adversaries. There's no earthly reason why we shouldn't collaborate on this. Benson and Black. Has a ring to it, don't you think?'

Black shrugged noncommittally. His eyes were downcast, not wishing to meet the bulbous gaze of the other. Was this another ploy? More deceit, more mocking trickery?

'The Authority, as you've probably gathered, are very interested in this case.' Benson tapped the folder once again. 'They're of the opinion that Q is a mystic.'

'I should have thought that was obvious,' Black commented dryly.

'They also believe—' Benson placed his sharp elbows on the table and leaned slowly forward '—that he comes from the future.'

Black stared at him. His first thought was that this was some kind of test. His loyalty was in question and it was Benson's job to sound him out. He said carefully, holding his voice steady, 'That wouldn't seem to be a logikal deduction.'

'Logik isn't everything,' Benson said flippantly. And then, adding treachery to his blasphemy: 'There are some of us who believe that Logik holds back progress.'

'Is that sentiment contained in the latest directive?' Black said, keeping strictly within the limits of MDA protocol.

Benson smiled briefly, as if humouring a child's naïve curiosity. 'It's a non-official view shared by a number of people. However, as for the patient himself, the Authority have been sufficiently – shall we say intrigued by the reports so far submitted as to grant that this other world of which Q speaks might possibly be our world several hundred, maybe several thousand, years in the future. They point out that he did arrive in rather unusual circumstances: he was many miles from any land formation when the ship picked him up, and we have no other explanation, other than Q's own, of how he got there.'

Black was aware that he had begun to breathe heavily. He cleared his throat nervously before speaking. 'This all sounds very irregular to me. By a process of logikal thought we shouldn't be concerned in the slightest how he arrived or where he comes from. Our concern is, or should be, with the present. Q is here, he exhibits strange symptoms – that and only that should be our field of investigation.'

'What a pompous little man you are,' Benson said, smiling faintly. He clasped one bony hand in the other and cracked his lean knuckles.

'Pompous perhaps, but correct,' Black said stiffly. His hatred for Benson fed upon itself, a deep gnawing pit of hunger which had to be filled, which craved to be appeased. He sensed a trap; all this loose easy talk was meant to lull him into relaxing his guard and inadvertently betraying himself. But he wouldn't be caught. It would take someone far cleverer than Benson to catch him out. He said, 'Have the MDA seen all the reports?'

'All except this one.'

'And they conclude there's some truth in his story.'

'They conclude nothing. They've merely put forward the idea.'

'The idea?' Black said incredulously. 'They've put forward an *idea*?'

'Ideas are in vogue, or hadn't you heard?' Benson was smirking openly. 'I forgot: you aren't, of course, privy to the confidential minutes of Court business. Great pity, they make fascinating reading.'

Black's grasp on reality was slipping. With the panic of uncertainty came a feeling he sometimes had that the entire world was in conspiracy against him, everyone sharing some colossal joke at his expense. People who smiled at him he suspected of plotting in secret, giggling and snorting with hilarity behind closed doors. They all knew something he didn't, had invented a monstrous subterfuge with which to fool him, and all the while he was the trusting innocent, taking it in, honest and credulous to the point of imbecility. At times he expected those around him (Benson, the guards, even the inmates) to collapse in helpless laughter, with him as the focal point of their insane amusement. He had that feeling now, watching Benson's smirking grin; it was as if the world was about to tumble around his ears like a house of cards.

'And if Q is from the future,' he managed to say. 'What then?'

'Use your imagination, man.'

Imagination, Black thought. More blasphemy!

'The Court is of the opinion that the patient should be thoroughly investigated. We should seek to learn all we can, and if possible devise a method for testing the validity of his statement.'

'You don't seem to understand,' Black said. Frustration chafed him like a constricting rope. 'It's quite evident from the reports that Q doesn't believe in this world. He thinks of us as products of his imagination, that we're projections, and only exist through him. There's only one way to prove him wrong.'

Benson's large watery eyes gazed at him unblinkingly. 'I hope you don't mean what I think you mean.'

'What other way is there?'

'I don't think,' Benson said deliberately, 'I like your attitude.'

'Stuff what you think. This is my patient. I conducted the initial experiments. You've become involved because you see it as an easy way of making a quick reputation. Not so long ago you were all for bunging him in the High Intensity Complex and letting him rot. You've soon changed your tune.' Black's forehead felt hot, yet the back of his neck was cold and clammy. Had he gone too far? He didn't care. He was sick of being patronized by this thin stick with the bulging eyes and bobbing Adam's apple. Come the purge, come the cogging purge . . .

Benson stood up abruptly. 'I'm sorry you feel like this,' he said in a tone that meant he wasn't. 'I was hoping we could work together. But if you want to be stubborn, two can play at that game.'

Black felt a chill of apprehension. Everything was moving too fast, he couldn't keep a check on it all. Why was Benson offering him this opportunity? Benson and Black. It did, after all, the more he thought about it, have a certain ring to it.

Perhaps he had been hasty. Yes, on reflection perhaps he had. Benson was doing the decent thing, he was prepared to share the credit with a colleague. And why not? Their relationship in the sanatorium had always been cordial, professional and one of mutual respect. They had worked together in the past, they would continue to work together in the—

'I shall put in a request for your immediate transfer to HIC. I've gone out of my way to be fair, but you won't have it; very well. Be it on your own head.'

'What have I done now?' Black said whiningly. 'Tell me what I've done first. It's not fair otherwise.'

'Oh yes,' Benson said, jerking his head vigorously. 'You'd like that, wouldn't you, you'd lap it up,' and suddenly screamed at the top of his voice, 'You've had your last swinting chance, you gingy crole!'

Black swayed back in the chair, faint and puking ill.

Q was indeed a shadow of his former self. He lay in rags and tatters in the shadowed corner of the small room, a slanting grille of sunlight imprinted on the wall above his head, his feet lost in the evil-smelling straw which littered the packed earth floor. For much of the time he chatted with Prosser and Stratters, though Johnny kept pestering him to play a game of chess. He replied, untruthfully, that he had forgotten how to play. The truth was that he hated a game to be interrupted by a call to 'scramble' over the tannoy: his mind couldn't accommodate a cerebral exercise and the adrenalin-pumping action of chasing the Hun over the fields of France in direct sequence, one after the other. So he preferred to chat idly and read the *London Illustrated News* in the lulls. The round-backed wicker chairs were comfortable, and sometimes he fell asleep in the hot French sun. Prosser took his photograph once and they got the film developed in the nearby town of Châlons-sur-Marne, showing him sprawled out fast asleep with his flying jacket and mouth open. It was the hottest summer he could remember, so stifling that sometimes he had difficulty breathing.

The bright rectangle moved imperceptibly across the wall. From outside came sounds of shouted commands and shuffling feet: the deportees were being moved from the pre-screening compounds to their final destinations. Some would be sent to camps in the Western Province, some would join the labour gangs working on the construction of new camps, others would embark on the one-way trip north to the High Intensity Complex. The compounds had to be cleared within the day to make room for the new consignment – a bumper crop of six thousand which was at the moment disembarking at a number of ports on the southern coast. The recent purge had rooted out many more dissidents who, up until now, had masqueraded as model citizens. The King of New Amerika had instructed the Medikal Direktorate Authority to issue a new set of even stricter directives which in effect made anyone, under certain circumstances, liable for deportation. Nobody knew what those certain circumstances were. Even some of the Authority's own medikal staff had been caught in the net, and it was rumoured that not everyone at Court was above suspicion. Psy-Con was growing at a rate no one had anticipated; soon Australasia would be one vast concentration camp, filled from coast to coast, and in order to accommodate any more, the liquidation programme would have to be implemented. The Authority had been asked to suggest the simplest, cheapest and most effective methods of disposal, and this had provoked a lively debate in the medikal journals. One suggestion had been that they set up a breeding centre for two-headed King snakes, several thousand of which could be turned loose on the inmates; but it was pointed out that this would prove dangerous for the medikal staff and guards – besides which, the shrunken decomposing bodies would constitute a health hazard. Far better to extend the network of alligator pits; this method had the dual advantage of disposing of the corpses while at the same time ensuring that the alligators had a regular and nutritious diet.

Benson visited his prize inmate at least twice a day, noting with disquiet his mental and physical deterioration, which was more pronounced and more apparent almost by the hour. He wanted – rather he desperately needed – Black's medikal knowledge and expertise, but now that the fool had turned against him he would either have to take charge of the case himself (which he wasn't qualified to do) or seek advice from one of the resident medikal staff, a step he was loath to take. But it was clear that something had to be done and done quickly. The Authority wanted results, and an inmate wasting away to nothing wasn't likely to provide them. Benson himself didn't give much credence to the theory that Q was from the future: it was a notion arrived at by some flat-bottomed bigwig who spent all his time reading medikal reports and coming up with startling conclusions from the flimsiest of evidence.

Benson was finicky about smells, and the smell in the small square room was overwhelming, the mingling of stale air, the excrement of previous occupants and a peculiar, biting, caustic odour that reminded him of preserving fluid. The heat overlaid everything with a dense sultry stillness that caught at the back of the throat, and Benson remained near the door, not wishing to soil his black polished boots in the filthy straw. He held a scented handkerchief to his nose so that when he spoke his voice was muffled and nasal.

'Do you have any startling predictions for us, old man? We're agog to learn more about our fantastic future.' The tone of sarcasm was pained and rather weary: he couldn't bring himself to believe that this pitiful bundle of rags in the corner possessed the power of prophecy. In any case the future was confined to the future. It would arrive in good time, not a moment sooner.

A pale hand, practically transparent, moved among the straw. Benson made a sound signifying impatience and disgust. Nausea gathered in his throat like a thick congealing clot of blood. He said from behind the handkerchief: 'You're a lucky cuss if only you knew it. The rest of your batch have gone, been carted off, never to return, and here you are, still wallowing at His Majesty's pleasure in comfort and plenty. Aren't you the fortunate fellow.'

'Il est fort, ce Boche!'

'I beg your pardon?'

'God save the King.'

'That's more like it.' Benson shifted his weight from one polished boot to the other and made a fist to examine his fingernails. 'Well, I can't stand here chatting to you all day. Do you have anything to add to your previous statements? Are you, as a matter of interest, from the future or are we merely figments of your excitable imagination?' He snorted at his own humour.

Q said, 'If Stahl dies . . .'

'Stahl?' Benson said, frowning. 'Who is this mythical Stahl?'

'A composite identity.'

'You mean several people wrapped up in one body?'

'Something like that.'

'Something like that?' Benson said irritably. 'Either he is or he isn't.'

'He is and he isn't.'

'No no no,' Benson protested. 'Either he *is* or he *isn't*. You can't have it both ways.'

'But I can,' Q said mildly, looking at him with colourless eyes. 'Reality is in the eye of the beholder.'

'Very deeply significant, I'm sure. However, its meaning, if it has one, excapes me.' He leaned nonchalantly in the doorway, first making sure that it wouldn't mark his uniform. 'So, if Stahl dies, what then?'

'One of us will cease to exist.'

'One of us. You mean either you or me?'

'Yes.'

'Well, which one?'

'I don't know.'

'I assume it must be me. Somehow – by magic, presumably – I will suddenly vanish. One moment I'm here, the next, *pouf!*, gone. Where will I go to – heaven?'

'You will not go . . . anywhere.'

Benson giggled into the handkerchief. 'If I disappear from here I must appear somewhere else.'

'Not if you don't exist to begin with.'

'Oh, I see. You mean, this isn't really me? I'm not actually standing here in this filthy hole talking to a madman? This conversation is only taking place in my mind – I beg your pardon – *your* mind.'

The transparent hand moved feebly among the straw.

'Well, come on, man, which is it to be? Am I real or are you?

You don't seem very sure whether I exist through you or you exist through me. Or could it possibly be both? You seem to invent rules as and when it suits you.'

Q said, 'We each invent our own reality.'

Benson chuckled. 'In that case you haven't done too well from where I'm standing. Couldn't you think of anything better?' He gestured round the cramped, hot room, at the rectangle slipping down the wall, the stinking straw on the floor. He seemed highly amused.

'It all depends which reality you mean,' Q replied. 'Yours or mine.'

'I prefer mine,' Benson said, smirking behind the scented handkerchief.

'That's because you have no choice.'

'Don't presume too much,' Benson snapped, straightening up. 'You're a fine one to talk about lack of choice. Wherever you *think* you came from, the fact is you're here; there was plenty in your statements about how you arrived, but precious little about how you get back.' He said this with evident satisfaction. 'The Authority believe you're from the future, our future. Personally I have my doubts, but if you are from the future it would be in your best interests to say so.'

'Why?'

'Because if you are,' Benson said, nettled, 'the Authority are interested in your welfare. If you're not, then they couldn't care less what happens to you, and for the matter of that, neither could I. All this stuff you've spilled could be so much hot air, so much bilge, so much eyewash. Black might have been taken in by it, but I'm not.'

'This is hell nor are we out of it,' Q said quietly.

'Hell indeed for those who get stroppy.' Benson kicked at the straw pettishly. His moist eyes bulged over the clutched hankerchief. 'I'm being par-tic-u-lar-ly patient with you, my friend, whether you realize it or not. I could have you sent to the High Intensity Complex like that – ' he snapped his thin fingers ' – and what could you do about it? Nothing.'

'No,' said Q faintly, wasting away in the corner.

'I'm glad you appreciate the gravity of you predicament. If

there's anything I detest it's a smart-aleck inmate. They get short shrift from me, I can tell you. Bam, fizzle, and off with their heads!'

The yellow sun adopted a new position. The rectangle changed into a trapezium. Like the sun, Q was sinking fast, through the floor of the small square room. He couldn't sustain the image much longer; if help didn't arrive soon he was doomed to this world, trapped in an abstract spatio-temporal coordinate somewhere over the rainbow. (Prosser said, 'It won't surprise me if Stratters' gone. He's been rushing about the sky like a madman for the last five days. He's too inclined to rush into those bloody Huns.' They all agreed.) Benson's black shiny boots took all the light in the room and cast it back in smeared reflections. There was nothing the light could do to alter this state of affairs. It reminded Q that light was amoral, blameless, that it shone indifferently on the good and bad alike.

He said, 'We are held, you and I, in a state of entropic equilibrium: what the astro-technologists would call "a stasis situation". We can go neither forwards or backwards.'

'You're not going to have another fit, are you?' Benson asked, alarmed. 'One thing I can't stand at any price are frothing babblers.'

'Did you hear . . . did you understand what I said?'

'Yes I heard.'

'Did you *understand*?'

Benson scuffed the toe of his boot in the straw. 'Some of it I did,' he said. 'Not all of it. Some of it'

'We are stuck here, you and I,' Q said deliberately, 'until the machine decides to release us. She has created a stasis situation in which we are held captive, progressing neither forwards or backwards. The most we can hope for is a continuous repetition of events; perhaps this is the first time this conversation has taken place in this room, or it may be the sixth, or it may be the ten millionth. We have no way of knowing. We shall replay this scene until she decides to change it – or end it.' He added, very softly, 'If only I could remember how it ends.'

Benson was breathing heavily into the handkerchief. 'I understood,' he said with great emphasis, 'I definitely understood from your previous statements that Stahl was responsible for all this. Isn't that what you said? Am I being obtuse? You said that Stahl's mythic projection had created Earth IVn. Where and how does the machine come into it?'

'Stahl was connected to the machine. His brain impulses were cyberthetically processed. It was the machine's, not his, mythic projection; and the cyberthetic system in the Vehicle projected the same image. All cyberthetic systems are part of the one collective machine consciousness.'

'Fascinating,' Benson said, 'cod-laddle.'

'As you please.'

'You're asking me – *expecting* me – to believe that Earth IVn and everything in it is the imaginative leap of a machine?' He blew out a gust of air, signifying incredulity.

'Except that this isn't Earth IVn.' Q laid each word down gently, as if it might break. 'I come from Earth IVn. This, I'm afraid, is an imitation, and not a very good one, at that.'

Benson shook his head wonderingly. 'Where do you get it all from? How can you expect me to believe such a ridiculous story? In your last statement, if I remember it correctly, you said that the machine had been destroyed. All that was left of it was the craft you were picked up in by the *Slave Trader*.'

'The machine was destroyed in mythic projection. She still exists somewhere – I don't know where – in another region of spacetime.'

'Mmmm,' said Benson. 'Very interesting, I'm sure. It would be even more interesting if I understood a single word of it. And as for the cock-eyed notion that you come from Earth IVn . . . well, I'm stumped. I've been led to believe that you *arrived* here, not departed from it.'

'You should never assume anything without proof.'

'How true,' Benson said, grinning into the handkerchief. 'Which leads me to ask what proof you can provide for any part of what you've told me. There isn't a scrap, as far as I can see.' He was arrogant in his smugness.

'Except the most convincing proof of all.'

'Which is?'

'That I'm here.'

'You are certainly that all right,' said Benson grimly.

There was no moon that night. The pre-screening compounds were silent and deserted, awaiting the new consignment of deportees on the morrow. The guards were absent from their posts, carousing in the wooden mess hall, and so it was easy to smuggle the snake into the medikal enclosure, holding the heavy lumpy canvas bag by the rope wound tightly round the crimped neck, and carrying it swiftly and silently across the soft warm sand. Black felt like a schoolboy up to a naughty prank. He would have rubbed his hands with glee had they not been otherwise engaged. Two-headed King snakes were deadly venomous and the exercise required the greatest diligence and concentration.

He stayed close to the huts, hugging the bleached and weathered boards and dodging across the open spaces, even though all was silent and blackness. He had memorized the location of the hut in which Q was being held; it would need care, because they all looked alike in the darkness and he didn't want to poison some poor innocent.

He dodged across the last remaining space, flattening himself against the boards, and his heart seized up in his chest. He could hear voices! He stood, hardly breathing, and listened, and felt a surge of secret exultation. One of them was Benson's and the other, softer, weaker voice could only belong to Q. Black smiled. He would kill two birds with one stone. It seemed almost providential that King snakes should have two heads – one for each of them.

. . . Now, this had to be done quickly and with the utmost caution, without either of them being aware of what was happening. It had to appear an accident; not the slightest hint of suspicion must fall on him. In the morning he would be wakened and told the sad news, and already he had decided on a suitable expression: shock and disbelief, and perhaps a vague suggestion of sorrow as the news began to take hold. He was annoyed that it would mean going without breakfast, but a man distraught with grief for a dearly-beloved dead colleague would hardly set to with a healthy appetite. Anyway, he'd make up for it at lunchtime.

He placed the canvas bag on the sand, and at once the bag came alive and started to jerk and writhe. Goodness, what vicious creatures they were. And so nasty and repellent he was almost tempted to believe that someone had dreamed them up in a nightmare. The low murmur of voices went on. Black listened but couldn't make out what was being said. It was of no importance anyway: they would soon be gone from this world, leaving nothing behind but the yellow shrunken husks of their former selves. He opened the outer screen door of the hut leading to a narrow passageway with several doors opening off it. There was no guard on duty (a breach of regulations) and the passageway was dim and smoky from the flickering oil lamps suspended from the ceiling. Holding the bag away from him, he stepped inside, allowing the screen door to close softly behind, and moved stealthily forward, the bag alive and writhing in his grasp. This was the tricky bit. He went over the sequence once again, for the umpteenth time:

1. Unfasten the rope and hold the neck of the bag closed.
2. Open the door.
3. Throw the bag inside.
4. Close the door and hold it shut.
5. Wait until all sounds of struggle have ceased.

There would be cries of course, probably screams as well. But there was no one within earshot, and with the drunken racket the guards were making it didn't matter anyway. He shuddered and licked his dry lips. The pity of it was that he wouldn't be able to watch. He would have to be content with listening and using his imagination. Luckily he had plenty of that, imagination. Just as well the Authority didn't know. Tee-hee. He unfastened the rope, holding the neck of the bag closed (1), opened the door (2), threw the bag inside (3), closed the door and held it shut (4), and waited until sounds of struggle had ceased (5).

9

The Cup Might Smash . . .

"Milton Blake said, 'I'm glad to have this opportunity of talking with you and your staff, Johann. I think it's important that we review the program and update ourselves on the current situation.'

The Director said, 'I think you know everyone. Shall we sit down? I've arranged to have coffee sent in.' He added, 'Though I must say I prefer something less noxious, with a gentle sideways smile at Blake.

'I don't see why we had to meet in here,' Karla Ritblat said, sitting primly near the window. 'Your office, Johann, or mine would have been more suitable.'

'I wanted Milton to see the graphic displays,' Karve said. 'And they should make any explanation simpler and easier to comprehend.'

There were eleven people assembled in the TFC Lab: Johann Karve and his MyTT Research staff, Milton Blake and his personal assistant – a young, attractive, dark-haired woman with a shy smile – who hadn't yet been introduced. The displays were mounted on huge sheets of tinted silicate fitted to an apparatus which could be revolved to bring the appropriate display into position. From a control console the Director could animate sections of the display and use them to illustrate various concepts of Minkowskian geometry which were otherwise impossible to visualize; a cyberthetic input and printout unit was linked to the console to provide a real-time computation/induction facility.

Karve operated the shutters and the room blacked out, to be dominated by the display area with its brilliantly coloured markers, graphs and three-dimensional representations.

'Isn't money wonderful?' Blake exclaimed, awed and envious, which provoked laughter from the MyTT people. He exchanged glances with his assistant, who raised her eyebrows in rueful agreement.

The main display showed the inertial frame of reference Theta^2 Orionis in M.42. Karve leaned forward and touched the controls, bringing up a light trace which assumed an orbit round the companion collapsar 2U0525–06. It made a very pretty picture.

Karve began: 'By local standard time of the sat-Con-lab, whose orbit we have here, injection took place nine days ago, which on our time-scale is thirteen months. In that time – I'm sorry, in *their* time – they were able to maintain contact for three of those nine days, which far exceeded our expectations. Everything seemed to be going perfectly, there was no Vehicle malfunction, the cyberthetic system was doing everything we could have asked of her. The Vehicle was held in stasis on the periphery of the event horizon, all systems were checked, and then she was released from the influence of the Dyson EM Sphere. From that point onwards we had hoped to estimate the Vehicle's relative time and location by means of the Neuron Processer.' He touched the controls and another display revolved into position. 'This is the Vehicle's track immediately prior to deep injection, and as you can see it's perfectly stable. We knew we were about to lose contact but it was hoped that our predictive capability would at least allow us to calculate the approximate spatio-temporal coordinate.'

'We were juggling with probabilities,' Karla Riblat put in, with bleak rectitude.

'We were indeed,' Karve agreed. 'But the probability of locating the Vehicle at a given coordinate was better than fifty-fifty, which we all agreed were the best odds we were ever going to get.'

'Was NELLIE on line at this point?' Milton Blake asked.

'Ever since pre-injection. We thought that if we fed everything we had into her, every scrap of information, then she'd be better equipped to make a few intelligent guesses.'

'And she made quite a few,' Castel said. He turned his thin, narrow face to Blake, the reflected light of the display catching the bony protuberances of his forehead and jaw. He said, almost in a tone of apology, 'I must admit to having been one of the doubting Thomases, Milton, as regards your box of tricks. I thought we were getting dangerously near the voodoo drums and chicken entrails approach, but I take some of it back.'

'But not all of it,' Blake said, smiling.

'I don't see how I can, under the circumstances.'

Blake's assistant said, 'We never tried to hide the fact that NELLIE was prototype equipment. It was a calculated risk all along.'

'Indeed, indeed,' Karve said. 'And I don't think post-mortem recriminations are necessary; they're certainly of no scientific value.' He touched the controls once again. 'We tracked the Vehicle into the third day, and then lost her. Nobody's fault, nobody to blame, it was what we expected. From this point on we had to rely on the Neuron Processer, which was linked directly to a terminal here in the TFC Lab. Data started to come through almost at once, within a matter of weeks, which on the Vehicle's time-scale would equate to minutes. It was garbled and difficult to interpret – again as we had anticipated – but the system *was* functioning and we *were* receiving a random scatter of images, some of which were very interesting, not to say intriguing. It was the very devil of a job to collate them and make an assessment of their validity, but we did our best.' He paused. 'The responsibility for this fell to Professor Castel, who I think did a tremendous job, bearing in mind that it was our first attempt to analyse the results of post-injection feedback. We had at least a coherent if fragmentary picture of what was actually taking place inside Temporal Flux – not at all a mean achievement in my estimation.'

'I'm flattered by your tribute, Director,' Castel said. 'However, I think all of us realize that our individual contributions wouldn't have amounted to much if it hadn't been for the painful and harrowing experience that Chris underwent.'

There were murmurs of agreement and Karve said, 'None of us, I'm sure, would want to minimize his particular contribution: it was indespensable and I know he realizes it.'

166

There was a lengthy silence which no one, it seemed, was keen to break, until the Director said, 'Isn't that so, Chris?'

'I believe we were all indispensable, Johann. It was never at any time a one-man project.' Queghan looked from face to face in the dim light. 'Even the cyberthetic system must share some of the credit.'

'Machines, machines,' Castel said lugubriously. 'They're our blessing and our curse. They limit us and extend us.'

Blake said, 'You speak of the Project in the past tense, Chris. I wasn't aware that it had been terminated.' He looked questioningly at the Director.

'It isn't terminated in the strict sense of the word, and won't be,' Karve said. 'We'll maintain the link with the Control lab and record anything that moves, so the Project is on-going in that sense. But as for keeping Chris in permanent mythic projection in Psycho-Med I don't believe that's necessary any more, besides which it's not a pleasant experience. To artificially stimulate and prolong an epileptic fit could seriously affect long-term mental stability, and that's one machine we can't replace, not at any price.'

'In terms of injection – on his time-scale – he hasn't been there very long,' Milton Blake said. 'Nine days, I think you said.'

Karve was prepared to admit that it could, conceivably, be even less than that. 'It might be hours, minutes, maybe a few seconds. We honestly don't know. Time dilation in that region of spacetime is impossible to calculate.'

'But we're keeping all channels open?'

Karve nodded. 'Absolutely. If Martin or the Vehicle are releasing data of any description we'll process through NELLIE, relay down here to the TFC Lab and plug Chris into the terminal point. Anything he comes up with on the cyberthetic printout will be interpreted by Professor Castel. After thirteen months it's become standard procedure.'

Quegan looked at him quickly, thinking that it was a phrase he hadn't heard the Director use before; but after all, it was an ordinary phrase that anyone might use. A lot of people did use it.

Milton Blake's young assistant said, 'Was contact with Brenton lost suddenly, at a precise world-point, or did it tail off . . . sort of fade away?'

'As you'll know from the extracts—' He looked from the girl to Milton Blake.

'I'm sorry,' Milton Blake apologized. His teeth flashed brilliantly against the mass-black of his skin, itself lost in the dimness of the room. 'Dr Hallam, my personal assistant. Zandra Hallam.'

'You'll have noted from the extracts, Dr Hallam, that right from the beginning contact was erratic and incomplete. We picked up a lot of stuff we couldn't interpret or fit into the overall pattern and even now we don't know how much of the information is valid; we can only trust that Martin – Professor Brenton – stayed reasonably close to the projection as processed.'

'Are you saying that contact was lost abruptly or over a period?'

'I'm saying that I can't give you a definite yes or no either way.' Queghan smiled at her. 'Is it personal interest, or is it important that you know?'

Zandra Hallam frowned and caught Milton Blake's eye. It seemed as if a signal had passed between them: a question from her which he had acknowledged and confirmed. She said, 'How important or significant this is I'm not sure. The patient died a few days ago. He reacted violently as though someone had injected a virulent poison into him.'

'And you assumed that loss of contact with Brenton coincided with the death of your patient,' Castel said, his large protruding eyes swivelling from Blake to his assistant.

'Not quite that,' Zandra Hallam said. 'But if we were to look for meaningful coincidences, then that would seem to be a prime candidate. Stahl dying and loss of contact with the injectee might be causally connected.'

'I thought causality was in rather poor shape these days,' Queghan said. 'You might just as well point to an acausal connection for all the difference it makes.'

The Director spoke up. 'We shouldn't dismiss this without at least considering it. I don't think any of us can give satisfactory answers to the questions raised by post-injection; the more information we have, from whatever source, the more likely we are to make intelligent predictions as opposed to wild guesses.'

'I'd go alone with that,' Castel said. It occurred to Queghan that there were times when Castel was more concerned with having his voice heard than in making a positive contribution. Just as now – glancing round to make sure that people were paying attention, his hollowed face alert and serious, and below it the stringy neck with the prominent thyroid cartilage. His wispy, thinning hair was caught in the light like a solar flare round the dome-like skull. He said, 'As the only archivist present I feel I've got to be a little more pragmatic in my approach. And in what I'm prepared to accept,' he added, in mock-apology. 'Despite the success we've had with our mythic projection technique and the Neuron Processor, I find that I'm left with a fair amount of faith but very little proof. We think we know what happened to Brenton inside Temporal Flux: we *think* we know, but we have no direct evidence. As someone has already said, the feedback to date has been incomplete and difficult to interpret. But what if—' he looked at Queghan and raised his sparse eyebrows '– I'm sorry, Chris – what if none of it, not a scrap, is accurate? What if it's merely a random series of neurological impulses that have been scrambled cyberthetically, and Chris has been able to present them in some sort of rational, coherent order? In other words—'

'—there is no incontrovertible proof,' Queghan said, finishing the sentence for him and carrying the line of thought forward. 'We should be able to verify the results, but we can't: we have to accept what we're given. Isn't that what you're saying?'

'Yes,' Castel said. 'I'm asking for proof. There isn't so much as a scrap, that I can see.' His lips gleamed in the light from the display. 'In any TFC experiment there should be a method of verification, some means of checking independently of the main source whether or not the findings are accurate.' He gestured helplessly, a little show of humility. 'We simply have the one source which we either accept or reject; it's a matter of blind faith.'

'Not necessarily,' Queghan said. 'You're ignoring the fact that Brenton, wherever he is, is inhabiting any one of a series of mythical futures. *Any one of a series of mythical futures.* This means that the probability of his inhabiting any or all of them simultaneously is equally as valid. Therefore our mythic projection, being based on probability, is as accurate as it could possibly be. Brenton exists in a state of probability, which means that somewhere in spacetime the possibility exists that perhaps he wasn't injected into Temporal Flux at all. It might have been someone else: you, me, Professor Blake, Dr Hallam. We just happen to be inhabiting one possible tangent of an infinite series of probabilities – just as Brenton is. But because we don't know for certain which one it is, then he could be – he *is* – inhabiting any or all of them simultaneously.'

While coffee was being served Castel edged in to Zandra Hallam, and Milton Blake drew Queghan to one side. He said: 'I want your honest opinion, Chris. Do you think Stahl's death has any connection, causal or otherwise, with Project Tempus? You gave Dr Hallam a hard time earlier on.'

'It could have and it couldn't.'

'That's not much of an answer.'

'It's the only one I can give you,' Queghan said. 'My honest opinion is that I honestly don't know. He died suddenly?'

'Yes.'

'Caused by . . .'

'There you have *me*,' Milton Blake said. 'I suppose you could describe it as shock. But what kind of shock I don't know. It could have been fear, it could have been caused by an electric current—'

'By galvanology?'

Milton Blake smiled. 'That possibility hadn't escaped *me*. Yes, by galvanology. Or as the result of a snake bite.'

'I see. That's what Dr Hallam meant when she referred to injection by a virulent poison.' Queghan stared into space. There was something bothering him, a tiny niggle of doubt that hovered on the edge of his understanding and refused to come into focus. Stahl had projected the red ocean: was it a world he had invented and Brenton had entered or had it always existed, existed even now, and Brenton was trapped in it? If the former were true, it would mean that this other world had ceased to exist. It would simply vanish, dissolve into nothingness, leaving Brenton in limbo. Queghan experienced the feeling he sometimes had of just having woken from a dream which he only dimly perceived and faultily remembered. In this particular dream – an alternative scenario – it wasn't Brenton who had been injected into Temporal Flux, but himself. And that was another possibility too, Queghan realized, just as valid. Was there no way to prove the truth or falseness of either proposition? Perhaps both were equally true, equally false; it all depended from which point of view you happened to be observing the same set of events.

Milton Blake said, 'What do you think the chances are of retrieval?' His intelligent brown eyes were fixed intently on Queghan.

'As always, fifty-fifty,' Queghan said. 'They will never improve, never deteriorate. As long as Martin's location remains a probability rather than a certainty he will be held in perfect equilibrium, progressing neither forwards or backwards. Perhaps he's in a cyclic situation, living through a chain of events which repeat themselves endlessly; we have no way of knowing.'

'And if there is a causal connection between Stahl's death and Brenton's injection into Temporal Flux?'

'Martin will know about it, but I don't see how we ever can – unless he returns.'

'The more we find out, the more there is to know,' Milton Blake said. 'We ask a big question expecting a big answer, and all that happens is that we're faced with bigger questions demanding bigger answers.'

'We have the Report,' Queghan said, indicating the fat block of mimeographed sheets bound in black vinyl. 'We've also shown that Neuron Processing is a valuable technique in post-injection evaluation. In your second-generation machine you might surprise us even more.'

'This is the complete Report?' Milton Blake said, opening the cover.

'As transcribed and interpreted by Professor Castel, with appendices and reference sources. You've seen the extracts?'

'They were sent to us as they came through; but it would be useful to have the final and official text on file. It bears detailed study.' He turned to the first page and began to read:

> ' "The vessel cleaved through the red ocean, the purple foam churning and frothing in its wake. It was a three-masted barque, square-rigged on the fore- and main-mast, schooner-rigged on the mizzen, with yellow vinyl sails, its prow a whorled piece of timber painted white in the shape of a unicorn's horn: the *Slave Trader*, seventeen days out of London Toun bound for New Amerika in this, the ninth year of the reign of Our Most Gracious . . ." '

Blake paused and glanced up. 'Interesting style.'

'Franz rather fancies himself as a literary mythographer,' Queghan said, smiling.

'Franz?'

'Professor Castel.'

'I don't object to it so long as it doesn't distort the truth,' Milton Blake said, though he looked none too happy.

'Truth is subjective. This happens to be one man's interpretation. Through someone else's eyes it would appear quite different. It's even possible' – Queghan raised his white eyebrows and smiled – 'that we're the mythic projection of someone in another region of spacetime. They could be observing us at this moment, eavesdropping on our conversation, trying to figure out the strange antics of those peculiar creatures on Earth IVn.'

Oria was in the garden with the child when he returned home. The youngster was tottering about on sturdy seventeen-month-old legs chasing insects and sunbeams and laughing when he took a tumble. Rain was due later that evening, but they had at least an hour's sunshine before the first drops were scheduled to fall. Oria was sitting bare-legged on the grass, the slender set of her shoulders now in keeping with the rest of her frame, her fine yellow hair pulled back in bunches which gave her the manner and appearance of a mischievous schoolgirl. She was tanned, clear-blue-eyed, and happy as a sandboy.

She said: 'Do you suppose that when they made this planet they knew we were going to live here?'

'They might have peeked into their crystal ball and seen a thousand years hence,' Queghan conceded. 'But I think it more likely that they wanted to replicate Old Earth as near as was technologically feasible. The first two weren't a tremendous success; it took some time to organize the bioplasm to become self-generating and self-supporting.'

'But those were planetary states,' Oria said. 'They merely looked for suitable planets and tried to adapt them to earthlike conditions; we can take some pride in being entirely man-made.'

'The planetoidal state does have a few things going for it,' Queghan said, picking up the child. 'One of them being that this fine fellow will grow up thinking of himself as a citizen of the world instead of trying to prove that his patch of dirt is superior to anyone else's.'

'That doesn't defeat the problem,' Oria pointed out wisely. 'It simply moves it up the scale. He'll probably try to prove that his ball of dirt is superior to anyone else's.'

The child struggled to be released and Queghan set him down on the grass. He ran off, chasing a butterfly.

Oria said, 'Would you like a drink?'

'No, thanks. I'll just rest awhile.' He stretched out on the striped lounger and closed his eyes so that the sun filled his eyelids with a warm, kindly glow. He was tired. The trouble with mythic projection was that it disoriented the sense of time and place. He remembered what he had said to Blake about Martin Brenton: 'Perhaps he's in a cyclic situation, living through a chain of events which repeat themselves endlessly; we have no way of knowing.' He had that feeling now – of having lived a number of alternative lives simultaneously, of having lived *this* life before. It was an interesting speculation, but he was too weary to pursue it. In any case, there was no way of arriving at a definite conclusion: a man could only occupy a certain world-point at any given moment. The fact that he might, in a universe of probability, have occupied some other world-point was logically sound but impossible to prove. I'm here, sitting on the lounger in the garden, my consciousness tells me so, Queghan thought; now if I'm somewhere else at this same moment, my other consciousness, belonging to my other self, will also confirm my presence there. It will be unaware of this self, this consciousness, except in these same terms of abstract speculation. Perhaps the two separate consciousnesses – the several, an infinite number of them – are at this moment involved in this same speculation, each aware of the possible existence of the others but unable to prove or refute their actual reality.

He smiled in his semi-waking state of tranquillity as the word appeared in his mind. Of course it had no objective, empirical meaning. 'We each invent our own reality,' as he had once said to someone a long time ago.

The boy was chuckling, and when Queghan opened his eyes he saw that Oria had rolled a coloured ball to him which, in narrowly evading his reach, had caused him to topple sideways on to the grass like a fat wobbly doll. He lay, helpless and out of breath with laughter, an arm and a leg waving comically as he tried to regain his balance.

Would any of this have been altered, Queghan wondered, if he and not Brenton had been selected for injection into Temporal Flux? How would the alternative scenario have read with a cast of characters shifted one to the left? In a private aside, Johann Karve had confided to him that Project Tempus was finished. His exact words had been: 'It's over and done with. Martin, wherever he exists, is beyond our help'. And Queghan, for all his powers of mythic projection, failed to visualize that other place: it was well and truly down the rabbit hole, through the one-way membrane, beyond the event horizon.

Oria stood before him twirling a golden flower. The grass grew between her toes. She knelt down and held the buttercup underneath his chin, saying the old nursery rhyme: 'Do you like butter? Do you like cheese? Yes is a smile. No is a sneeze.'

The child sneezed, making them both laugh.

'Do you think he's a mythographer in the making?' Oria asked.

'God, I hope not,' Queghan answered. 'I wouldn't wish that fate on my own worst enemy.'

'Speaking of which,' Oria said lightly, 'I've invited Castel to dinner tomorrow evening.'

Queghan groaned. 'Castel isn't an enemy,' he said. 'He's much worse: a bore.'

'I feel sorry for him.'

'I think you secretly desire him.'

'Naturally; but I thought we'd agreed not to mention that.'

Queghan suddenly needed the reassurance of commonplace intimacies. His hands went around her waist and slid down inside the top of her skirt to hold the firm globes of her buttocks, the thumb of his left hand seeking the dark-brown mole on her right cheek. It was a tiny but significant landmark, one of the many which guided him through the day and proved to him the realness of his own existence. Without them he would have floundered, become lost and drifting in a grey, featureless dream.

Just as now, the human race, spreading outwards on the stepping-stones of natural and man-made planets, also clung to comforting reminders of the birth-planet which had no more substance than that of a collective racial memory. Mankind's original home had entered mythology, become an ancient legend like Old Earth's own legends of primitive civilizations. So in order to preserve it they had fashioned their new homes in the likeness of Old Earth, shaping the continents and oceans in its image.

On starlit nights Queghan sometimes sought out the 4th magnitude star which was the original Sun, the one that had given birth to human life. Its light still travelled across space, to be collected in the retina of his eye, even though the star itself had for a long time become dull and fat with premature old age, a red giant in the incipient stages of nuclear decay. The small speck of light he saw now was of the Sun in its prime, many centuries Pre-Colonization: he was in effect looking backwards in time to an age when human beings had just begun to heave themselves off the planet, first of all in crude flying machines and then in small pieces of space hardware. The exact point in time was impossible to define, though Queghan liked to imagine it was round about – give or take a century or two – the time of the Second World War; this appealed to the romantic aspect in his nature and made a convenient link with his specialist study of the period.

But the eerie paradox of looking backwards to the age of his ancestors never diminished or failed to thrill him. His own antecedents were alive then, carrying his blueprint in the cells of their bodies. In however bizarre a form, he had lived through that time too, been present at every stage of human evolution.

Oria said, 'It's starting to rain.'

The clouds had formed according to plan, shutting out the sun, and the air became suddenly chill as the light faded. Queghan shivered and experienced a twinge of pain: an ache in his left shoulder where the strange pale mark was imprinted in the flesh. He picked up the child and with his wife went up to the house."

IO

'There Shall Be Time No Longer'

Black reached forward awkwardly and closed the folder which lay on the trestle-table. The exertion made him grunt and pant, as a mangy dog struggling on the end of a chain. The heat in the room was at the point of being unbearable; it was only made tolerable by the knowledge that one could not escape it; it filled this ghastly continent from ocean to ocean, a dense humid blanket resting immovably on the flat desert scrubland.

He eased his position slightly. Mustn't overtax the old ticker, not in this heat. Two events had profoundly disturbed him, the second of which had compounded the first. The first event had been the arrival of the guard that morning to inform him of an unfortunate accident: the yellow shrivelled corpse of the King's Special Envoy had been discovered in one of the interrogation cells. It was clear (there was no other explanation) that he had been bitten by a King snake. 'These things happen,' the guard had shrugged, while Black quickly remembered and composed his features to convey shock and disbelief with a vague suggestion of sorrow at the tragic occurrence.

'Yes,' he had replied at last, 'what a tremendous shame,' and then waited politely for the guard to complete the catalogue of horror. When he didn't, and was about to withdraw, Black rashly inquired after the other occupant of the cell. The guard said, 'And who would that be, sir?' and Black said impetuously, 'Surely he wasn't there alone, not at that time of night. He must have been *with* someone.' The guard shrugged again and made a gesture comprising two asymmetric shapes in the air. 'We found only one corpse. His insignia identified him as an officer of the King's Commission. Should there have been someone else?'

177

And now there was the report, which Black assumed could only have been compiled some hours before the 'tragic occurrence'. It had been waiting for him on the trestle-table, lying there accusingly like a mocking jibe from beyond the grave, demanding to be read. It had at first mystified him, even made him laugh (though laughing was difficult under the circumstances) and then – as the realization dawned – confirmed his own worst fears. The worst fear of all was that Q's crazy prediction would come to pass – and yet it hadn't, not yet. But what had happened to the body? Q had vanished, ceased to exist, become a phantom hovering uneasily on the edge of memory. That was the first unsettling event.

The second was the reading of the report, which seemed to be saying that Brenton and not Q had been 'injected' into this world. If this were true it would at least explain how Q had managed to disappear from the cell: he had vanished because he had never been there in the first place. Instead Brenton had been the injectee (Brenton? Benson? Which was which?), and this being so it meant that everything Black experienced was a product of Brenton's (Benson's?) imagination.

But how ludicrous . . . he was letting this thing run away with him. He couldn't possibly depend on Benson/Brenton for his existence, not possibly. Brenton/Benson was dead. Dead. And he was alive. (He wished the girl wouldn't wriggle so.) To suppose that Benton/Brenson had imagined all this was to fall prey to the wildest imaginative leap of all. No, no, he would not accept it. Not when he had absolute proof (why wouldn't she keep still when he was trying to think?) that Bentson's/Brenon's dying had had not the slightest effect on the reality or otherwise of his own existence.

It might equally be proposed that he, Black, was responsible for this (ha-ha) future world of 'Queghan' and his laughable 'mythic projections'. Who was to say that one had the advantage over the other? Why, here, yes here, in the report – he wrenched the girl's head aside and reached over her shoulder to get at the folder – this Queghan fellow had voiced the doubt of his own reality, had mooted the possibility that he himself was the product of another consciousness. Yes, here it was, in black and white: *Perhaps the two separate consciousnesses – the several, an infinite number of them – are at this moment involved in this same speculation, each aware of the possible existence of the others but unable to prove or refute their actual reality.*

Ha! There it was. So let the cogging swints or Benon/Breston or whoever affirm or deny *that*. He was as real as they were. This moaning girl bent before him across the trestle-table was the only proof required. A jerking slippery poke from the rear gave the lie to all this bladdering cod-laddle, immersing himself up to the point of total penetration and hearing the choking gulp as the force of impact knocked the breath from her lungs. With each long sucking stroke he was entering deeper and deeper, the exquisite thrill making his sweating flanks tremble: an unbearable ecstasy rising to the pitch of a scream. She was moaning, he was coming, and as it flooded from him the yellow sun disintegrated in his brain, the red ocean bubbled up inside his head, and the world dissolved before his eyes into deepest impenetrable black.

APPENDIX 1:

Time Dilation

Time dilation – the 'stretching' or 'slowing down' of time – is a consequence of Einstein's Special Theory of Relativity, published in 1905. The Theory states, as a broad concept, that there is no absolute standard of reference throughout the universe; every measurement of phenomena depends upon the conditions under which the *observer* observes, not upon any intrinsic or objective quality which the phenomena contain. All observable results depend on the position of the observer at a certain point in spacetime, and all interpretations are equally valid and correct. In simple terms, there is no 'objective' reality which exists independent of an observer.

Another proposition of the Theory, which has been tested and verified, is that lightspeed, however it is measured and irrespective of source, remains constant at 300,000 kilometres per second. This would seem to defy common sense, for what it means is that if two beams of light are receding in opposite directions, we would assume the sum total of their speeds to be twice the speed of light, or 2c (where c = lightspeed). But this is not so. According to the formula

$$\frac{c+c}{1+\frac{c^2}{c^2}}$$

we find the answer to be c (the speed of light).

Similarly, if two spacecraft are receding from each other, both travelling at 90 per cent the speed of light, common sense would indicate that their combined speed of recession is 180 per cent the speed of light, but again this is not the case. Using the formula

$$\frac{a+b}{1+\dfrac{ab}{c^2}}$$

(where a and b are the speeds of the two craft and c is the speed of light) we see that the total speed of their recession is *less* than the speed of light. In Earthbound terms this appears to be nonsense, but it is a fact which has been proven by various experiments and one that any space traveller will have to live with.

Two other effects are worth noting, concerning the mass of a moving body and its length. The faster a body travels, the more massive it becomes, compared to its mass at rest. As it approaches lightspeed the body increases in mass until at lightspeed itself the body is of infinite mass (and would require an engine of infinite power to push it forward). At the same time, the length of the object (a spacecraft, say) *decreases* as it approaches lightspeed. At lightspeed itself the spacecraft is of zero length, and for all practical purposes ceases to exist.

In order to measure time dilation on board a spacecraft – and everything will slow down, remember, including clocks and the ageing process of the astronaut – we multiply a given period (60 minutes Earthtime) by

$$\sqrt{\left(1-\frac{v^2}{c^2}\right)}$$

to arrive at the following table. This has been calculated for a spacecraft which on Earth measures 100 yards in length and taking one Earth hour as the standard time interval. From this it can be seen how the various effects operate upon a spacecraft approaching the speed of light.

It should be noted that these effects upon a spacecraft approaching lightspeed are identical to those experienced by a body in a strong gravitational field. In fact, Einstein, in his General Theory of Relativity, makes no distinction between the effects of speed and those of gravitation. A Vehicle in the vicinity of a Temporal Flux Centre would, for all practical purposes, be approaching lightspeed, and thus be subject to the effects tabulated below.

Speed of ship as percentage of light speed	Length of ship (yards)	Mass (tons)	Duration of ship-hour in minutes (Earth=60)
0	100·00	100·00	60·00
10	99·50	100·50	59·52
20	97·98	102·10	58·70
30	95·39	104·83	57·20
40	91·65	109·11	55·00
50	86·60	115·47	52·10
60	80·00	125·00	48·00
70	71·41	140·03	42·75
80	60·00	166·67	36·00
90	43·59	229·42	26·18
95	31·22	320·26	18·71
99	14·11	708·88	8·53
99·9	4·47	2,236·63	2·78
99·997	0·71	14,142·20	1·17
100	zero	infinity	zero

APPENDIX 11 :

Schwarzschild Radius (Rs)

In 1916, Karl Schwarzschild, one of the leading physicists of the time, calculated the effects a small, extremely massive body would have once it had passed below a certain critical radius – the Schwarzschild Radius (Rs). He found that it would distort spacetime so severely that nothing could ever escape its tremendous gravitational force.

Surrounding a body of this type would be the *event horizon*, so called because it is an absolute barrier to the outside universe, preventing any communication from inside the event horizon to the outside: not even light itself can escape.

To take a specific example, that of the Sun, how far would it have to contract before reaching the critical Schwarzschild Radius? The mathematics are as follows, where G is the gravitational constant, c is the velocity of light, and M a given mass:

$$Rs = \frac{2GM}{c^2}$$

Using SI units, where mass is measured in kilograms, length in metres, and time in seconds, $G = 6.7 \times 10^{-11}$ and $c = 3 \times 10^8$ metres per second. For the Sun, $M = 2 \times 10^{30}$ kilograms, and using the following calculation

$$Rs = \frac{2 \times 6.7 \times 10^{-11} \times 2 \times 10^{30}}{(3 \times 10^8)^2}$$

we find that the Sun (at present 700,000 kilometres) would have to be compressed to 3 kilometres to achieve its critical radius. By the same calculation, the entire mass of the Earth would have to be compressed into a volume less than one centimetre in radius – about the size of a marble – before entering a stage of Temporal Flux; or, as it might be known, a mini Black Hole.

ACKNOWLEDGMENTS

For the calculations used in Appendices I and II, I should like to thank Adrian Berry for permission to quote from his book *The Next Ten Thousand Years* (Jonathan Cape 1974); and my thanks also to Patrick Moore and Iain Nicolson for permission to use material from *Black Holes in Space* (Ocean Books 1974), and for their suggestion of the graphic 'ripple' analogy.

GLOSSARY OF TERMS

Conscious Universe: A theoretical concept, so far without any evidence to support it, which propounds that the 100,000 million galaxies in the observable universe constitute a single conscious intelligence, or hyper-brain.

Cosmology: The branch of metaphysics dealing with the universe and its relation to the mind.

Cyberthetic: Machine intelligence with a reasoning and deductive capability, ie a thinking machine.

Dream Tape: A means of plotting and recording (for later analysis) the varying patterns of sleep and dreaming activity by the use of a portable EEG device.

Dyson Electromagnetic Sphere: Construction of solid iron-ore asteroids which produces a one million volt electrical field to stabilize a region of Temporal Flux.

Electromagnetic Interference (EMI): A system utilizing electromagnetism and gravitational energy which permits interstellar travel by using the basic proposition of lightspeed as a constant; developed on the theories of Oliver Heavyside, nineteenth century electrical engineer.

Ernst–Ryan–Gathorne Experiment: Mathematical evidence for the acausal nature of time and the universe which demonstrates that Event A might precede Event B, or vice versa, at one and the same time – depending on the location of the observer.

Event Horizon: The absolute barrier surrounding a Temporal Flux Centre, preventing communication of any kind with the outside universe.

High Intensity Complex: An area of Psy-Con for deportees who have been screened and classified as high-risk subversives.

Indexer: A device for inducing and measuring mind rhythms, eg alpha, theta, delta, etc

Metagalaxy: A term which embraces all of Creation, ie that portion of the universe which is visible and the greater portion known as the Hidden Universe.

MetaPsychical Code: A theoretical framework which seeks to integrate all psi phenomena and human neurochemical data in one cohesive structure.

MetaPsychical Research: Similar objectives to the related science of Myth Technology but more concerned with an investigation of human neurochemistry and its connection with the 'celestial clockwork' of the Metagalaxy.

Mythic Projection: A state of 'Peak Experience' which gives an insight, almost religious in nature, into the mechanism of Creation. Known among ancient superstitious peoples as an epileptic fit.

Myth Technology: That branch of Cosmology (qv) which seeks to relate all psi phenomena and mythic projection with the four prime energy sources of the universe.

MyTT (Myth Technology Research Institute): The central organization dealing with theoretical and applied research into mythical past and future events (repositories of knowledge).

NELLIE (Neuron Processer): Abbreviation of Neuron Processing and Transfer/Three-Dimensional Display Interface developed in PSYCON for purposes of projecting brain patterns into visual display.

Neurological Landscape: A term used in MetaPsychical Research to denote the overall picture produced by a patient during transmission of brain patterns (cf NELLIE).

Observable Universe: The Hubble Radius of 13,000 million light years containing an estimated 3,000,000,000 galaxies.

Planetary State: A naturally-occurring planet colonized by man.

Planetoidal State: A man-made body which has been formed, shaped and set in orbit for the purposes of colonization.

Pre-Colonization: The entire period of human history prior to man's colonization of other worlds.

Project Tempus: A program of collaboration between the planetary and planetoidal states whose aim is the practical investigation and exploration of Temporal Flux Centres by means of manned injection.

Psycho-Med: Faculty of MyTT concerned with the psychological and physical preparation of the injectee prior to injection into Temporal Flux.

Psy-Con: Psychological Concentration Camp organized and run by the MDA, situated on the continent of Australasia.

PSYCON: Psychic Conservation Unit, the medical-experimental department of the Faculty of MetaPsychical Research.

sat-Con-lab: satellite-Control laboratory orbiting on the periphery of a Temporal Flux region for command of and communication with Injection Vehicle.

Scenario Planning Symposium: A conference of related sciences with the aim of establishing a cohesive policy for further research, in particular in relation to Project Tempus.

Schwarzschild Radius: See Appendix II.

Singularity: The region of infinite spacetime curvature at the dead centre of Temporal Flux where matter has been crushed out of existence and time has stopped.

Tachyon: Sub-atomic particle which travels faster than lightspeed and is therefore 'time-reversing'. Theoretically believed to be the basis for the precognitive faculty in human beings of future events.

Temporal Flux Centre: A region of infinite spacetime curvature (cf Singularity) resulting from the collapse of an extremely massive star to within the critical Schwarzschild Radius.

Temporal Flux Injection Vehicle: A spacetime craft endowed with cyberthetic intelligence capable of entering the ergosphere of a Temporal Flux Centre.

TFC Lab: Temporal Flux Centre Laboratory, the nerve-centre through which all data are processed and instructions relayed.

Theory of Synchronicity: As developed by Carl Jung and Wolfgang Pauli, the theory states that psi phenomena are examples of 'meaningful coincidences' which are linked in terms of meaning but have *no causal relationship* such that one thing or event gives rise to another.

Time Dilation: See Appendix I.

Time Throat: An area within a Temporal Flux Centre which leads to a mutiplicity of alternative universes.

REFERENCE SOURCES

ASIMOV, Isaac: *Adding a Dimension* (Dennis Dobson, 1966)

ASIMOV, Isaac: *From Earth to Heaven* (Dennis Dobson, 1968)

ASIMOV, Isaac: *The Neutrino* (Dennis Dobson, 1966)

BERRY, Adrian: *The Next Ten Thousand Years* (Jonathan Cape, 1974)

BRONOWSKI, J.: *The Ascent of Man* (BBC, 1973)

BURR, Harold Saxton: *Blueprint for Immortality* (Neville Spearman, 1972)

DOSTOEVSKY, Fyodor: *The Idiot* (published 1868)

DUNNE, J. W.: *An Experiment With Time* (Faber and Faber, 1927)

HOFFMANN, Banesh: *Albert Einstein* (Hart-Davis MacGibbon, 1973)

Index of Possibilities (Clanose Publishers, 1974)

JOHN, Laurie (Ed): *Cosmology Now* (BBC, 1973)

KARVE, Johann: *The Hidden Universe* (IV Sdp Edition)

KUZNETSOV, Boris: *Einstein and Dostoevsky* (Hutchinson Educational, 1972)

Lay Guide to Myth Technology (VII Sdp Edition, 3rd Revision)

MONOD, Jacques: *Chance and Necessity* (Collins, 1972)

MOORE, Patrick and Iain Nicolson: *Black Holes in Space* (Ocean Books, 1974)

MOORE, Patrick: *The Story of Astronomy* (Macdonald & Company, 1972)

SAGAN, Carl: *The Cosmic Connection* (Hodder and Stoughton, 1974)

SPINAR, Zdeněk V.: *Life Before Man* (Thames and Hudson, 1972)

TAYLOR, John: *Black Holes: The End of the Universe?* (Souvenir Press, 1973)

UNDERWOOD, Peter: *Into the Occult* (Harrap, 1972)

WHITROW, J. G.: *What Is Time?* (Thames and Hudson, 1972)

WILSON, Colin: *The Occult* (Hodder and Stoughton, 1971)

Panther Science Fiction – A Selection from the World's Best
S.F. List